WITHDRAWN
L. R. COLLEGE LIBRARY

WITHDRAWN

INSIGHT

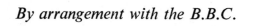
By arrangement with the B.B.C.

INSIGHT

DR. J. BRONOWSKI

HARPER & ROW, PUBLISHERS

NEW YORK AND EVANSTON

CARL A. RUDISILL LIBRARY
LENOIR RHYNE COLLEGE

501
B78i

48,907
Feb., 1965

Copyright © 1964 by Dr. J. Bronowski
First Edition

Library of Congress catalog card number: 64-19950

PRINTED IN GREAT BRITAIN

CONTENTS

INTRODUCTION

The chapters of this book show a series of cross-sections through modern science. But they do not present science in the usual way, as a register of isolated discoveries. Instead, my aim has been to present science in a new way, more difficult but more rewarding—as a web of ideas.

This, then, is a book of ideas: the strong and stimulating ideas which underlie science in the twentieth century. All scientific ideas are, of course, practical—they are judged by results; and in this sense, the ideas in this book have proved their power by the practical use to which they have been put. But they also have a power which is unexpected, namely to fire and to delight the mind by their hidden simplicity. I hope that the chapters which follow show how simple are the deep ideas of contemporary science, and yet how richly they combine.

A book of ideas has the advantage that it can range through many different sciences, and trace the common threads that link them. There is a good deal about human and animal life in these chapters, and about human and animal minds, as well as about dead nature. And this is right, because it is the way that science has been moving in the twentieth century. Physics and chemistry no longer have the monopoly of exact thought; they have been joined by (and to) biology and the study of behaviour and of mental processes. I have drawn my examples freely from all these fields.

One basic idea that runs through all the sciences today is the idea of evolution, which was first thought of in biology. We now recognise that living things are not alone in having evolved from simple beginnings to their high and integrated complexity. Dead matter also evolves in time, step by step, from simple to complex; even the atoms of physics are all built up in the stars constantly from units of hydrogen. And at the other extreme, in the human mind, the gifts of reason and imagination are also built up from simple units, step by step from birth onwards.

There is an element of chance in every process of evolution. The simple units move at random, hit or miss, and only if the right ones meet in the same place at the same time do they lock together to form a stable structure. Yet this disorderly jostle of chance encounters does build up more and more complex relations, and creates an order. It is another new and universal idea in science that order on the large scale is made from disorder on the small scale. And then in time, every large order will fall apart, by the erosion of chance, to its underlying dance of disorder. That is the very nature of time.

These ideas force us to think out afresh what we mean by time, and also by space. Here, surely, are the most fascinating questions that science has yet asked. Time is an order of events, as an onlooker sees them; but does every onlooker see them in the same order? Or can time run differently for two onlookers—for one who moves with the events, and one who stays at home? Can two men age at different rates? This strange question can now be put to the test of experiment, and one of my chapters describes that minute and beautiful experiment.

Space also expresses an order: the order of the parts in a complex structure, which locks and holds them together. This is a geometrical and indeed a visual idea, which runs through all science today. It is the idea that everything in nature is put together from its units as a building is put together, brick by brick—so that what matters is not the bricks but the architecture, the way they are put together. The most telling idea that I find in science now is that the behaviour of all things is governed by their inner structure. All nature is a process, and what changes in the process is the arrangement of the same building blocks.

The architecture of nature is a universal idea, which stretches far beyond the fields of science. I find it expressed as concretely and vividly in the arts as in the sciences. Therefore I have included the arts in my last chapter, and have looked for the same idea in contemporary sculpture, in the novel, and in architecture itself. There is, I think, a single vision in all these creative activities, and it is right to call it *The Vision of Our Age*.

I use the word 'vision' deliberately here. This book shows that the discoveries of modern science spring from and are linked by a small number of profound and original ideas. And these ideas are not humdrum working rules of the laboratory; they are unexpected and deeply imaginative ways of looking at the world afresh. Science in our age is not a book of facts or of methods, but a vision of nature.

There is another reason why I use the word 'vision'. The reader who has turned the page once to come with me as far as this will already be aware that mine is a strongly visual imagination. It was therefore natural to me to present these ideas from the first in words and pictures together. The chapters of this book follow roughly (and much more fully) the sequence of a series of television programmes which I gave under the general title *Insight*. I have kept that characteristic title for this book, and I have also taken the illustrations from the television programmes.

The achievements of science deserve our admiration. We live in an age of great discoveries, and they are changing our lives deeply and swiftly. Our daily environment is being transformed as we watch it: we work at different jobs, we move about in different ways, we use our leisure differently. We have new sources of energy, and new means of control and communication, which enlarge our command of nature from day to day.

And our command is not only of dead nature; we are learning something more revolutionary, and that is to command living nature. We can prevent or cure diseases that used to haunt our childhood. We know how to fight infection and decay. We are coming to understand how the body ages, and the mind with it, so that we can begin to push old age back. Link by link, we are unravelling the long chain of minute processes which make up life.

Yet the greatest of these achievements is always the unravelling. Our triumphs are rooted in the understanding of nature. We command her with new ideas, and this book is a testimony to the power and beauty of modern ideas.

PART ONE—SIMPLE BEGINNINGS

1

A CHILD DISCOVERS THE WORLD

We are aware of the world through our five senses. This is true of the everyday happenings round us, and it is also true of the experiments that we make in science. We may look through a microscope or listen to a Geiger counter, we may set up the most delicate apparatus, but in the end what we record has to enter our minds directly through the senses.

But what the senses report does not have a meaning in itself. In itself, each message is piecemeal and unordered. We form a picture of the world only as we learn to link one message with another, to relate what the eye sees to what the hand touches, and so to build a unity from the simple parts. This is how science forms its picture of nature, and it is how every human being forms a picture of his own world. Science does not find its discoveries waiting for it, ready-made, just as a child does not find reality waiting for it, ready-made. A child has to discover reality for itself, by building from simple to more complex experiences. All learning is a process of building up a picture of the world—an active picture within which we know how to move and behave. That is the lesson of this chapter; and it is as true of the new-born child as of the searching scientist.

The picture on the right was taken just after the birth of a baby. It was taken literally from the baby's point of view, but it would be misleading to say it was what the baby saw. Nobody reading this book will have any difficulty in identifying things in the picture. There is a nurse wearing a mask, a door-knob, a keyhole, a light. But if you are reading this book, then nurses, masks, keyholes and lights, are familiar things. You have seen them all before. A new-born baby has seen none of them. It has seen nothing, heard nothing, tasted nothing, smelled nothing, and felt nothing. The pattern of light and dark that it sees does not make a coherent picture. The sounds it hears are meaningless. In the words of the philosopher William James, the baby's world is a 'blooming buzzing confusion'.

The baby needs to learn everything from the beginning, and at first it cannot even be taught. It must learn by itself, first by chance happenings and

9

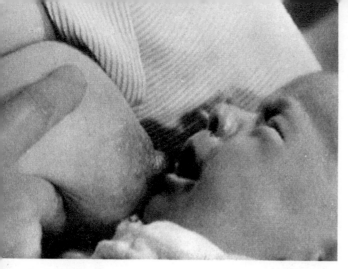

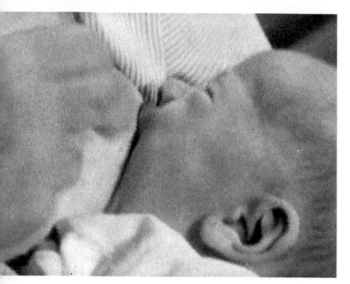

The only things the three-day old baby in the pictures can distinguish are pain and pleasure. The only thing it knows is its mother's breast, and it has not even learned to suck that properly. If it is removed from the breast it will cry, but it is not crying for the breast—it does not yet know what it wants. The three-day old baby cries only because it suddenly feels discomfort.

It will be several weeks before the baby learns to look for the mother's breast with a definite purpose. Even then, its movements are still unco-ordinated: it has no plan for getting what it wants. But it knows what it wants—at about five weeks the baby has a purpose, to get its mouth round the mother's nipple. And this is a specific purpose, something much more definite and more active than a mere feeling of discomfort when it is hungry. The baby's hands and mouth at five weeks will still explore at random, but they know very well what they are looking for. Purpose gives a direction to search, and is the first step in all human endeavour.

During the next few months the most important things that the growing baby learns is to co-ordinate its senses. The four-month old baby in the picture below still moves mainly at random. Its eyes are not following anything. Its hands touch by accident. But all the time it is learning. From the accidental coming together of its hands, it learns to connect the movements that it makes with the sensation of its hands touching. Each time that the hands touch, the hand-touching movement becomes a little easier. Eventually the baby is able to touch its hands whenever it wants to. It can do it by choice.

It seems very simple to us that a baby should learn to move its right hand and its left hand at will so that they may meet. But it seems simple only because we have been through it all: we have learned to be at home with the co-ordination of the body. In the

then from its own experiments. Step by step, it builds up a picture of the world slowly, and learns to relate its own sensations to external events.

We have all built up our pictures of the world in this way, although none of us can remember how it happened. But we can learn a great deal by watching it happen in others. We can see how the basic ideas about the world, which we all share, are formed. So we can gain an understanding of how the human mind, at first only able to distinguish between pleasure and pain, can develop its great powers.

We may also get some insight into our own minds. Insight may be defined here very simply as being able to see the wood in spite of the trees. To most of us this is difficult. Our minds are so cluttered up with preconceived ideas and prejudices that much of what lies beneath the surface is hidden from us. But children have not had time to form many prejudices, and from their questions we may come to question old ideas of our own which we used to regard as self-evident.

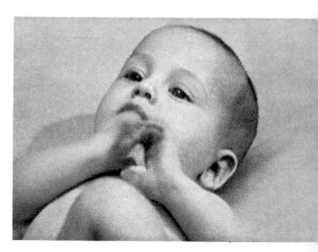

development of the baby, however, mind and body together, this is an enormous step. It locks two parts of experience together—the experience of the right hand with the experience of the left hand. All the complex building up of experience, step by step, will go in this way, by joining two different messages into one. And this process of learning to co-ordinate the different messages is always active. Neither the child nor the adult, not even the scientist, simply observes the world. They explore the world in action.

This baby is six months old. It follows the swinging beads with its eyes and reaches out for them with its hands. It cannot quite reach them, but it has learned to reach for them—it has learned that things which can be seen can also be touched. In the same way, people who have been blind from birth and who are given sight by an operation also have difficulty in co-ordinating sight and touch. They may not at first be able to recognise objects they have handled many times.

The pictures above show babies between nine and ten months old. Not only can they put their mouth to the bottle—when the bottle falls over they know how to get it back. They can reach for bricks and pick them up. Yet notice that at this age the baby

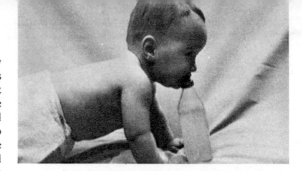

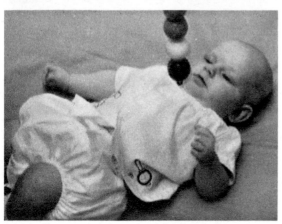

still does not distinguish between its hands and feet properly. It tries to use them both in the same way to pick things up. And it still puts things in its mouth. Its mouth was the first organ it used to explore the world and is still important.

In their actions, these babies have made their first discovery about the world. They have discovered space. By learning to co-ordinate their senses, particularly sight and touch, they have invented space for themselves. Like scientists, they make their discoveries through creative activity. They do more than simply look at the world and record what they see, like a photograph. They experiment, and just as a scientific theory is based on experiments, so is a baby's picture of the world. At first the picture is crude; as the baby grows, so the picture also is refined and elaborated, and takes more and more things into account.

Space is a baby's first great discovery about the world. The second is objects. To a very young baby things which are not present, which cannot be seen or heard or felt, simply do not exist. The discovery that objects continue to exist even when they are hidden may take many months of experimenting.

Look at the four-month old baby in the pictures below. It is interested in the toy and it is crawling towards it. Yet as soon as the toy is hidden, the baby at once loses interest completely. At four months, the toy is not an object with an independent existence; it is merely a bundle of sense impressions. Each time the toy is given to the baby it is a completely new thing, a different bundle of impressions on each occasion. When the toy is hidden it does not exist.

The baby above is nine months old and it has learned about hidden things. It cannot see the sweet inside the paper but it knows it is there. It can unwrap the sweet and put it in its mouth.

Once a child has realised that even when an object is hidden it is still there, it starts a new stage in its development—separating the world from itself. The child begins to see the world filled with people and objects, among which it is itself one. Up till now the child has been learning to manipulate objects with its hands. Now it can start to manipulate them in thought. It has entered the gateway to imagination and reason.

Manipulating objects in thought, imagination, is the third great step in the child's growth towards understanding. The child takes part in an everyday happening and then it transfers things that it sees and hears and feels to its inner experience. It makes images. This power of imagination distinguishes man from other animals.

We use the word 'imagination' by habit to mean something odd and fanciful; we often contrast it with what is real, and even with what can be thought rational. Indeed, imagination is commonly taken to be a way of thinking which is at the opposite extreme from scientific thinking. This is quite wrong. All thinking requires imagination—that is, requires us to form images of things which are not present at that moment. The child has taken the first step in the use of the imagination when it has learned to be aware of the existence of a thing which has been put out of sight—out of the immediate field of the senses. From then on, all thought rests on the formation of such images. Thought and imagination are inseparable, and both are characteristically human.

A child's image of a thing is derived from reality, but it does not correspond to reality in the same way as a photograph. For example, this drawing of trees by a child does not look like a photograph of

trees; yet it is not therefore a bad drawing. That would be a pointless standard to apply to it. The child is not making mistakes. It is drawing its image of a tree, not the tree itself. The drawing shows that the image is clear and well-formed. Each tree has a straight trunk with bark on the outside. On top of the trunk is a round blob covered with spots. The essential parts of the image, the aspects of the tree that the child has selected as meaningful to itself, are there in all the drawings.

A child growing up in our society gradually modifies its images of objects until they correspond to what might be described as photographic reality. But this has not always been so. It took hundreds of years for western European civilisation to learn to draw photographically. Early medieval pictures are as much images as the child's drawing of a tree. A photograph now seems more real to us than an early painting, but some primitive people are unable to recognise photographs of familiar things.

So when children play imaginary games, at being fathers and mothers, for example, or doctors and nurses, or at building a house, they are not out of touch with reality. On the contrary, they are trying imaginatively to enter a reality which they have only seen from the outside. They are exploring what it feels like to be grown-up, to run the show, to be important. Take a snatch of dialogue from a recording of two children at play. They are playing the sort of game all children play, under a table in the dining room, when everything in the room stands for something else. These children are playing at catching a bird. Notice how everything they say reflects the picture each has of his own place in the world.

Dig—dig a big hole
Now let me dig the hole—
No—no—you're not—no—I dig the hole—
The shovel's too big for you—I have to dig the hole—

After this difference of opinion about who is going to do the digging with the imaginary shovel, there are the problems of the imaginary rope.

Wanna hold the rope?
Yes
Well then hold the rope the right way—
You're not holding it the right way
What?
It's supposed to curl right up—
What?
It has to twirl right up—
I can't hear you—
Stop in the hole—

Somewhere the children have seen people digging a hole together. They have seen a rope held and they have heard about catching birds. These things became the raw material for their game of co-operation and rivalry.

Imagination is not something irrational. On the contrary, all reasoning is based on images we make in our heads. Some of the most difficult discoveries in science have in fact been made by men who saw, with child-like clarity, that nature might have a different logic from that to which we had accustomed ourselves. This is how relativity was discovered, and this is how the quantum of physics was discovered—by men who pushed aside the commonplace acceptance of the appearance of things and looked imaginatively for a deeper logic. Here are some pictures of two boys learning the logic of a toy which works when the right button is pressed. They are not learn-

ing mechanically, as a laboratory mouse might learn such a task. Their pleasure in learning is bound up with the imaginative nature of the game they are playing.

The older boy is four years old, the younger three. The toy they have is a double jack-in-the-box. If a jack is pushed down inside the box and the lid closed it stays closed. There is a button which releases the lid and lets the jack spring up again.

In the first picture the older boy starts to experiment. He does not know how the box works, but he is going to find out.

He did it very quick . . . put your hand on the back of there. . . .

When the younger boy begins to lose interest, a sweet is put on each of the jacks-in-the-box. His interest revives at once.

Look . . now you push them back in . . .

Next, the whole thing is turned into a game. The children put the sweets on the jacks themselves. The older boy goes through the whole ritual. He puts the sweet on the jack, pushes it into the box, closes the lid, and opens it again before eating the sweet in the third picture. But the younger boy cannot see the need for this obedience to the rules. He puts his

sweet on the jack and then eats it, or tries to—the older boy is stopping him in the fifth picture. And in fact, the younger boy does not learn the trick or logic of opening the box. When he pushes the button, it is still by accident; and in the last picture, he has stopped trying.

We have now followed a child through the three great steps in its early development. First we have seen how it co-ordinates its actions and thereby invents space for itself. Then we have seen how it learns that a cup or a table or a doll is still the same thing whether it is the right way up, upside down, or even hidden from sight. Lastly, we have now seen how the child learns to manipulate images as well as objects, and develops its powers through games and fantasies.

The process is one of building. Each step is put together from what has been learned before, until, step by step, the primitive bundle of sensations that is a baby at birth builds its vision of the world. Building complex structures from simple units is the theme of the first part of this book, and as we shall see, the physical world as well as the human mind develops in this way.

2

THE EVOLUTION OF MATTER

Science is divided into many specialised studies. A geologist does not expect to do research in mathematics, a chemist does not expect to work in biology, and a physicist does not expect to study psychology. Yet it is important to understand that all these studies are branches of science; they have in common the same basic outlook, the same way of seeing the world. The subject matter is different, but the guiding ideas and methods of science are the same in them all.

One of the basic ideas of science is that complex structures are built up from a few simple units. And the building is not done all at once: it takes place step by step, level by level, so that each level of complexity takes time to evolve from the level below. In essence, this is the idea of evolution that Charles Darwin invented in biology just over a hundred years ago. Since then, it has penetrated all the sciences. We have seen how it helps us to a fuller understanding of the development of a child's complex imagination. Now we shall turn boldly to the opposite extreme of science, to physics, and there we shall see again that the evolution of complex structures is a fundamental conception in modern science.

It has long been known that everything in the universe is made from the same few, basic materials. The stars, the earth, this book, and living things from the smallest virus to man himself, are all constructed from the same fundamental building bricks of matter. These bricks are the atoms of the different elements. There are rather fewer than a hundred elements in nature. Each of these elements consists

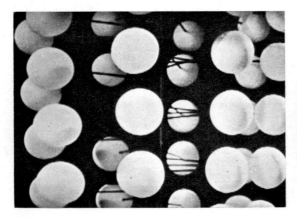 

of atoms of its own characteristic kind. So the universe is built of atoms of about a hundred different kinds.

A hundred is not a large number; but in fact, the number of essentially different units is even smaller than a hundred. For the different kinds of atom are themselves related, one to another, in a great family tree. The pictures on the previous page show the arrangement of the family tree in a schematic form. Each 'fruit' in the pictures is a characteristic atom of a different element. The elements which are related are vertically above one another on the same branch. The tree has eight such family branches. Hydrogen, the lightest and simplest atom of all, is at the root. As we go up a branch, the atoms get heavier and more complicated, but there is a definite family resemblance between the atoms in any one branch. The right-hand branch, for example, beginning with helium, contains the rare gases which occur in small quantities in the atmosphere. They share the peculiar property of not combining with other atoms.

Until this century, atoms were thought to be the ultimate pieces of matter: the smallest building bricks of all. It was thought at that time that matter could be split into smaller and smaller pieces, until each piece was an atom; after that, it could not be split further. The usual conception of an atom then was something hard, indivisible and indestructible. Atoms were atoms, and could not be created, changed or destroyed.

Now our picture of the atom is different. In a little over fifty years, a whole new world of sub-atomic physics has been opened. The atom is no longer an indivisible whole; it has a structure of its own. Instead of atoms as the ultimate pieces of matter, we have a number of smaller, fundamental units, from some of which the atoms are themselves put together. The idea of the unchangeable atom has gone forever. Today's fundamental particles appear, disappear, and even change one into another, in unexpected ways.

We know now that an atom consists of an inner kernel or nucleus, round which circle a number of electrons. The nature of the atom is fixed by its nucleus, and we shall therefore concern ourselves only with that; we shall pay no further attention to the screen of electrons.

As we have seen, the atom was first thought of as a single piece—that is why it was given its Greek name, *atom*, which means something that cannot be cut. After that, when the electron was discovered, it was thought that at least the nucleus of each atom is a single piece. Now we know that even this is not so; the nucleus also has a structure. It is built from two kinds of fundamental units: protons and neu-

trons. In the modern picture, these two kinds of fundamental particles are the ultimate units of nature.

In general, the nucleus contains protons and neutrons in about equal numbers, or roughly so. Yet what really fixes the nature of the nucleus is the number of protons. The atoms of any one element may contain different numbers of neutrons, but they all contain the same number of protons. That is what characterises an element: the number of protons in each of its atoms. For example, any atom whose nucleus contains only one proton is hydrogen. The first picture below represents a nucleus of ordinary hydrogen; it contains one proton and nothing else. The second picture is also hydrogen, because it contains only one proton—but it is heavy hydrogen (the kind of hydrogen in heavy water) because it also contains a neutron. The third picture is a nucleus of ordinary helium; it contains two protons and, incidentally, two neutrons. And so we go on up the scale. Any atom whose nucleus contains six

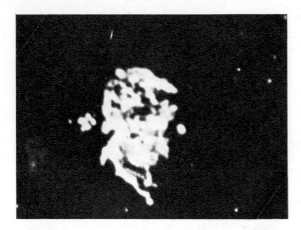

And the most complex elements are found in stars which have already exploded at least once. Our sun is such a star, whose material has already been through one stellar explosion.

Hydrogen is the raw material of the universe. It is by far the most common element. The stars are mainly hydrogen, and interstellar space is filled thinly with hydrogen. 'Filled' is a deceptive word here: the concentration of matter in empty space is far lower than in the best vacuum we can obtain on earth. But in the whole universe, this thin spread of hydrogen adds up to far more material than is contained in all the stars.

Our own solar system, our galaxy, all the galaxies together, swim in this sea of hydrogen nuclei—that is, of protons. But the sea is not uniformly spread out. It thickens here and there by chance. That is, in some places, concentrations of protons begin by chance. Then the attraction of their gravity pulls in more material, and a concentration grows larger, and gradually it makes a thicker concentration—a nebula such as that at the top of this page. This is the great nebula in Orion which contains as much material as thirty thousand stars, each the size of our own sun.

As the process of thickening goes on, the nebula in time becomes a star, or many stars. And now the build-up of atoms begins. A star spends most of its evolutionary life in turning hydrogen into helium. Take a fairly characteristic star: our own sun. The sun is only ninety-three million miles away, and the next nearest star is more than fifty thousand times as far off; so most of our knowledge of what goes on in stars comes from the sun. The pictures below, taken during a total eclipse of the sun, show the boiling and erupting surface which is the outward sign of the activity within. The energy by which we

protons is carbon. Twenty-six protons characterise a nucleus of iron. And ninety-two protons characterise the heaviest natural nucleus of all, that of uranium.

So atoms themselves have a structure. And since they have a structure, they can be constructed—and are constructed and reconstructed, in the stars. All the time throughout the universe complicated atoms are being built up from simpler ones.

That is, the nuclei of the different atoms have not been built up at some remote moment in the past, suddenly, all in one leap. They have evolved in time, and are still being evolved, one by one, upwards from the simplest nucleus of all—the nucleus of ordinary hydrogen, which is a single proton.

The evolution of the elements takes place in the stars, and stars of different ages build up different nuclei. A young star is busy taking the first step in the evolution of the elements: it builds hydrogen into helium. Older stars make more complex elements.

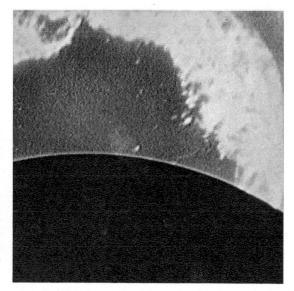

live comes from the sun, and the sun produces this energy by turning hydrogen into helium.

Helium was in fact discovered during an eclipse like this—the eclipse of 1868. A Frenchman, Paul Jannsen, and an Englishman, Norman Lockyer, observing that eclipse, recognised the trace of a new element in the sun which had not yet been found on earth. And the element was named *helium*, from the Greek word for the sun.

The fusing of hydrogen into helium can take place only at very high temperatures. So it starts in a new star only when the concentration of protons is pressed together by its own gravity so much that it heats to several million degrees. Now fusion begins; the star begins to give out energy, and it would fly apart if its own gravity did not manage just to hold it pressed together. The star settles down in this balanced state, which may last for tens or hundreds of millions of years.

However, the hydrogen in a star cannot last for ever. Eventually most of the hydrogen has been turned into helium, and this phase of the star's evolution comes to an end.

What happens next is complicated, and the net result is odd. The inside of the star usually contracts and gets hotter, while the outside of the star swells. The star becomes larger and visibly redder—a red giant. For example the star Betelgeuse is a red giant that can be seen with the naked eye.

A red giant has gained a new lease of life and it starts to turn helium into more complex nuclei. The helium nucleus, made up of two protons and (usually) two neutrons, is immensely stable. It now forms the raw material for the next stage in the evolution of the elements. Three helium nuclei now combine together to give a nucleus of carbon, which consists of six protons and (usually) six neutrons. Like the fusion of hydrogen into helium, this higher fusion also releases huge amounts of energy.

The fusion of elements from helium goes further. Oxygen, neon, magnesium, and all the elements up to iron, are built up at this stage. Iron has no fewer than twenty-six protons and (usually) thirty neutrons in the nucleus of each atom.

When it has made atoms as heavy as iron, or a little heavier, the star has used every source of nuclear energy. It can no longer produce fresh energy by fusion. Now it can no longer resist the forces of its own gravity which press it together. When it starts to contract now, it can tap no new source of nuclear energy to oppose the shrinking and prevent its own collapse.

At this stage, many stars throw out some of their matter. They get rid of material into space, and thereby scatter the elements that were built up inside

them. These elements may get incorporated into fresh stars. We have come to realise recently that our sun, and therefore our earth, contain many heavy elements which must already have been made in other stars. Our sun is not a young, new star; it is a second-generation star, which incorporates material from older stars.

Usually, the process by which a shrinking star gets rid of some of its material is gradual. But occasionally the process runs away catastrophically. Then a star hundreds of millions of years old collapses under its own gravity in a few hours. The result is a stupendous explosion. The star grows a million times brighter, and then it flies apart and the fragments slowly fade. Such an explosion is called a supernova. There are still in the sky today the visible traces of one such supernova explosion and this is shown in the picture below. This is the Crab nebula, which is the mass of gas, still expanding and still glowing, that is the remains of a supernova that exploded over nine hundred years ago.

The date of this supernova is known exactly; it was first seen on 4th July 1054. It must have been visible in Europe, but no-one recorded it there; Western astronomers at that time do not seem to have looked out of the window. The bright super-

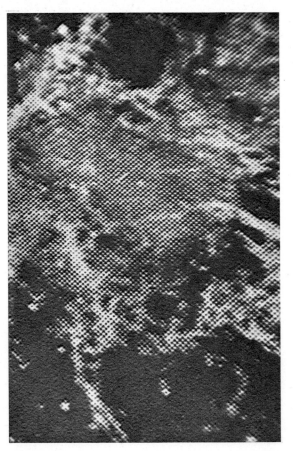

nova was recorded only by astronomers in Korea and China. The picture below is an account of it written by the astronomer-royal at the Korean court. He interprets the supernova as divine testimony that the country is happy in having so good a ruler.

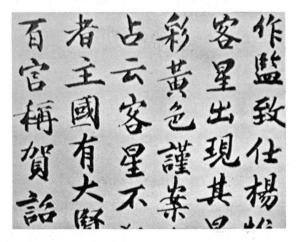

There have been two other supernovae in our galaxy, the Milky Way, in historical times. One of them was seen by the Danish astronomer Tycho Brahe in 1572. When this map of the constellation Cassiopeia was made, before 1603, the star on the left was still there, and brighter than any other. Today it

cannot be seen at all; it was a supernova, which has now faded.

The other supernova of historical times was that observed by Johann Kepler in 1604. Kepler records that it was first discovered, and his attention was drawn to it, by my namesake, the Czech astronomer Joannes Brunowski.

Supernovae are more than dramatic events in the night sky. They have a special part to play in the evolution of the elements. We have seen how the elements up to iron are built up in a star. Well over half the elements occurring on the earth and else-where are, however, much heavier than iron. These heavier and more complex elements are formed in supernovae.

Helium, the second most common element in the universe, is formed from hydrogen in all stars at some stage. The elements up to iron are then built up in the fairly common red giants. But it needs the fantastic forces of a supernova explosion to mould the heavier elements. A star gains energy by building the elements up to iron; but to form the elements much heavier than iron, it has to spend energy, and only a supernova can do that.

Supernovae scatter the heavy elements about the universe. So the interstellar dust contains small quantities of other elements besides hydrogen—some from supernovae, and some from other shrinking stars. The sun, and from it the earth and the other planets, have swept up some elements which have been formed in other stars and supernovae. The gold of a wedding ring here on earth must have been formed in the explosion of a supernova.

How do we identify these different elements in stars that we can never reach? How have we come to recognise that the stars are nuclear cauldrons? In a sense, this is merely a technical question; and yet, the answer is interesting because it goes to the heart of the process. The heart of the process is that the stars shine with an inner energy. This energy comes from the rebuilding of matter. We ought to be able to tell one kind of matter from another, one element from another, by the particular bands of energy which each radiates. And this is what we do: we recognise the band of energy—for example, the colour of light which each element radiates. Just as salt glows yellow if we throw it on the fire, just as a mercury lamp glows dull red while it is heating up, so the elements in the stars glow with characteristic colours. That is how Lockyer and Jannsen detected the new element helium in the sun.

These colours are not all in the visible band of light. Some of the characteristic wavelengths of the elements lie below the violet at one end of the spectrum, and some lie above the red at the other end. Such wavelengths are largely absorbed by the air, and in order to identify them we therefore need to rise above the air, in rockets and satellites. In its ordinary form, the instrument for detecting these characteristic wavelengths, the spectroscope, is too large to be carried in a rocket or a satellite. For this purpose, therefore, miniature spectroscopes have been developed which photograph small portions of the sun's spectrum at a time. The picture over the page shows one of these tiny instruments after it has been recovered from a rocket.

From photographs taken by these tiny instruments

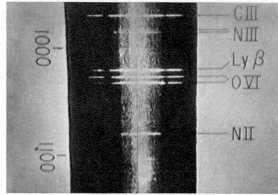

over the last ten years, it is possible to extend our knowledge of the sun's spectrum beyond the visible region. In the second picture above are lines in the ultra-violet which we cannot see on earth. Today such lines as these are the strongest evidence we have for the presence of many rare elements (such as neon) in the sun. It is the accumulation of such detailed evidence of many elements which now makes us certain that the sun is not a young star, but a second-generation star.

The elements were not formed once for all at some moment of creation. They evolved in the stars, step by step, by processes lasting hundreds of millions of years. Every natural process takes place in time, and the complex is later in time than the simple. The complex evolves from the simple, in the cauldron of a star as much as in the mind of a child. The most remarkable discovery in physics during our lifetime is that the hundred kinds of atoms, which a generation ago seemed to be the unchangeable building bricks of nature, have evolved by steps, from simple units to complex, all the way from hydrogen to uranium.

3

THE ARCHITECTURE OF LIFE

There is an order in nature: from simple to complex. And in that order, living things come higher and later than dead matter. Living things are more complex than dead matter. Of course they are; it is evident, as soon as we think about it, that a child is a more complicated being than a star. A child behaves in more complicated ways than a star. But the difference goes deeper than that. The very structure of a living substance, the way the atoms are arranged in it, is more complex than the structure of dead matter.

Both living things and dead matter are made from the same basic materials. Everything in the universe is made from the same fundamental particles, such as protons and neutrons. From the few fundamental particles are built up the atoms of the hundred or so different elements. And all the different forms of matter, living as well as dead, are different arrangements of these atoms.

Then how do living things differ from dead matter? Living things are made from the same elements as dead matter; the iron in the blood is the same as the iron in a motor car. And living things are built from atoms, just as dead matter is. Whatever difference there is can lie only in the arrangement of the atoms—in the architectural forms in which they are assembled.

Let us look, then, at a typical dead material: a crystal of salt. And, for contrast, we will look at a typical component of life: myoglobin, a component of muscle.

The first picture below shows the atomic architecture of common salt. Each dark ball represents an atom of sodium, each light ball an atom of chlorine. They form a simple, square, strong framework, in which each atom is held firmly in place by the six atoms round and above and below it. The way the framework is shaped gives salt its crystal form and its crunchy hardness.

The second picture shows a molecule of myoglobin. Complicated as it looks, it does not contain many different kinds of atom—only seven, of which the most important is carbon. The complexity is in the arrangement of the atoms; and it is this linked

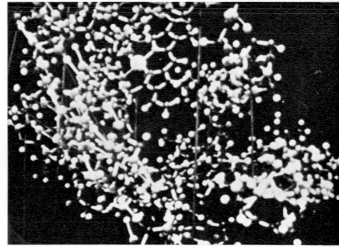

and coiled arrangement which makes it possible for myoglobin to play its essential part in the action of an animal's muscle.

Clearly, myoglobin is a much bigger and more complicated molecule than salt. It is so complicated that one might despair of finding the underlying order in it. But there is an order, and an order which is characteristic of all living things. The order comes from this: that a living molecule is assembled out of prefabricated units which are not just single atoms, but are themselves blocks of atoms held together in the same way. That is, the complex molecules of life are not just strings of atoms. They are themselves built up from a few basic molecules which nature has used as prefabricated units. The step from physics to biology is essentially the step from atoms to these prefabricated molecules which lie at the basis of life.

We will take in this chapter two important kinds of living molecules. One kind is the proteins, which are essential to living processes in the body. The other kind is the nucleic acids, which are essential to the processes by which life passes from one generation to the next. And we shall see how each complex kind, the proteins and the nucleic acids, is built from a few characteristic units—a few basic prefabricated molecules.

First, the proteins. There are many thousands of different proteins in the human body. Their appearances and their properties are quite different; for example, skin and hair and blood plasma and muscle are all made mainly of protein. Yet this large number of proteins, with their different behaviours, are all made up of different combinations of only about twenty prefabricated building blocks.

The building blocks for the proteins are called amino-acids. In all proteins, in all forms of life, there are only about twenty different kinds of amino-acids. They have standard linkages by which they join together across their ends to make proteins. It is as though there were a hook and an eye on each amino-acid molecule. Proteins are formed by engaging these hooks and eyes, as the picture below shows. That is, schematically the different kinds of amino-acid might be represented by the models here—five different kinds of them. And then a protein is made by hooking up a sequence of amino-acids, as in the picture at the top of the next column.

Although a protein is built of only a few amino-acids, a few kinds of building blocks, it contains these blocks over and over again. It is therefore

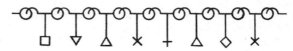

difficult to analyse the exact sequence in which the amino-acids are hooked together in a large protein. The first protein which was analysed was in fact a small one, but an important one. It was insulin, the hormone which diabetics do not make for themselves.

The structure of insulin was worked out chemically, by breaking the molecule into small pieces and identifying each piece. In the last years, another technique has been brought in from physics in order to find the general structure of protein molecules. The technique is particularly apt for finding the shape of a molecule, for it consists of firing X-rays at the molecule and seeing how the X-rays are then heaped up in some places and thinned out in others. For example, in X-ray studies of myoglobin (from which the structure on the last page was found) individual amino-acids cannot be identified, still less individual atoms; but the twists and turns of the molecule are vividly shown. This is something that no chemical analysis can reveal.

The shape of a protein molecule is important, and has profound effects on the properties of the protein. As the picture showed, in myoglobin the chain of amino-acids is twisted up into a ball. This is the arrangement also found in haemoglobin, the protein in the blood that transports oxygen about the body. There is the same arrangement in many of the proteins in blood plasma that play an important part in fighting infection. By contrast, in keratin (the protein in hair and skin and nails) the amino-acid chains are wound in a spiral like a coiled spring. In muscle tissue the molecules are long and fibrous, and when a muscle contracts the fibres slide past each other.

We turn now from the proteins to our second example, the nucleic acids. There is a high proportion of protein in any living organism. This is not true of the nucleic acids. There is some nucleic acid in every living cell, but the quantity is small. Nevertheless, the nucleic acids are fundamental to life. The most important of them, De-oxy-ribo-Nucleic Acid, usually called DNA for short, is the material which carries the hereditary instructions from one generation to the next.

There are only four kinds of basic building blocks

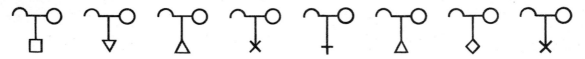

in the molecule of DNA. The picture below shows the actual arrangement of atoms in one of these prefabricated building blocks or units.

Each of the four units for DNA carries a hook and an eye, and links with its neighbour across an end. In this way, the units line up so that the parts of each unit which are characteristically different stick out from the main chain. The pictures show this arrangement in schematic form. What sticks out from the main backbone is the group of atoms, in each of the four units, which is characteristic for that unit.

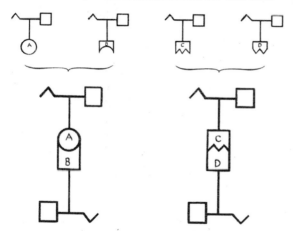

So far, what we have said about the architecture of life is no more than a description. These are the facts: these are the kinds of molecules, these are the ways in which they are arranged. But why? What is the function, what is the purpose of these arrangements?

In short, what is the nature of life that requires these geometrical structures? When we watch a child at play, we can sense from our experience the direction of its development, and we understand how its simple gestures are building up the more complex arrangements of behaviour. When we follow the evolution of stars, we can reason how the more and more complex atoms are built, and what their place is in the pyramid of matter. But so far, we have seen nothing in these patterns of living molecules to show why they should form the building blocks of life. Indeed, what is life?

What is life? That is rather too large a question for this or any other book. And even to ask, more modestly, what are all the characteristics of life, would still be too ambitious. But we can fasten on one characteristic which already stands out clearly from what we have said. The child in our first chapter follows the development of all children, and will pass that development on to others. That is, the living child will ultimately reproduce itself, directly or indirectly. By contrast, a helium atom in a star, though it follows the development of other helium atoms, will not reproduce itself.

The characteristic property of life which we single out here is, that living things reproduce themselves. This is a puzzling talent, for which it is not easy to find a mechanism. It is easy enough to find a machine which reproduces something—a minting machine reproduces pennies, a typewriter reproduces the letters of the alphabet. But a typewriter does not reproduce typewriters—and, to take the analogy more seriously, a penny is not able to reproduce pennies. If we were to take impressions of a penny, by any means, we would not get pennies but pieces hollowed out in the opposite way.

In short, any mechanism that we know which acts as a pattern or template produces, not things like itself, but things shaped in the opposite way. So any mechanism of atoms, molecules, amino-acids and so on that we can conceive would make copies not of itself, but of something shaped in the opposite way.

This was the puzzle of life until a few years ago. Then it was found that the building blocks of life owe their importance to the fact that they can be assembled into arrangements which can reproduce themselves. The basic molecules of life are as they are because only so can they act as a template and as a copy at one and the same time. This is a fundamental discovery in the architecture of life.

The mechanism is this. In all living cells, the DNA chains occur in pairs, wrapped round each other in a double spiral, as in the first picture on the next page. The two chains are joined by the characteristic groups of atoms that stick out from each unit. Thus each unit on one chain is paired with a unit on the other chain, and the paired units are marked by the characteristic groups of atoms which stick out of them.

The pairing is not random. Let us call the four units or building blocks of DNA by the letters a, b, c, d. Then a unit or block of type a cannot pair with just any one of b, c and d. The unit a can pair with

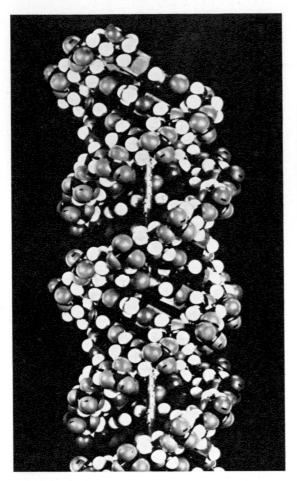

istics are passed on from one generation to the next when any living thing reproduces itself.

There are good reasons for believing that the hereditary instructions are contained in the thread-like chromosomes found in all living cells. This picture, taken through the microscope, shows the

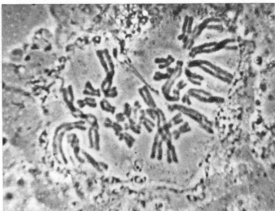

chromosomes in a plant cell. This next series of pictures shows what happens when the plant cell divides in two. The chromosomes uncoil and split

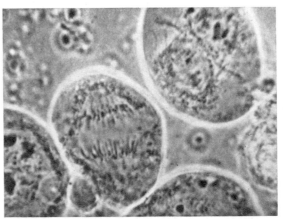

only one of them—say *b*. In the same way, *c* can only pair with *d*. We can make an imaginary model for this by representing *a*, *b*, *c* and *d* by geometrical shapes which lock together in pairs, like pieces of a jig-saw. The picture below shows such a model.

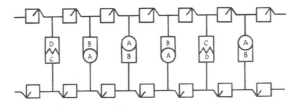

Because of this pairing, the building blocks or units on one chain completely determine the units on the other. For example, suppose part of one chain has its units in the order *d b a b c a*. Since *d* is always paired with *c*, and *b* is always paired with *a*, it follows that the matching part of the other chain has its units in the order *c a b a d b*.

This structure of DNA is not just an interesting chemical fact. It is of profound importance in explaining the mechanism of heredity—how character-

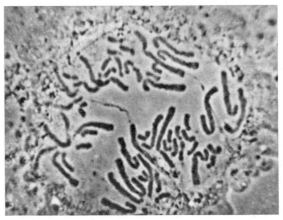

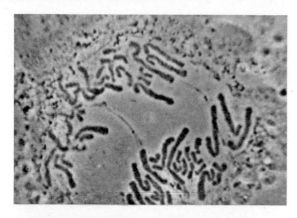

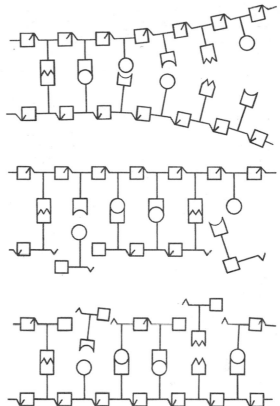

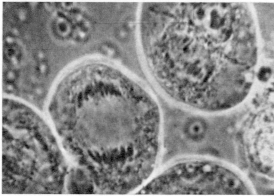

down their lengths, and half of each chromosome goes to each of the two new cells. In the new cells, the half chromosomes must rebuild themselves into complete chromosomes again. For when one of the new cells comes to divide again, its chromosomes look exactly like those of the original cell, and they uncoil and split down their lengths in the same way.

Most of the DNA in a cell is in the chromosomes, and must take part in the events in the series of pictures. We believe that the uncoiling and splitting of the chromosomes is the unravelling of the two strands in the DNA molecules they contain. One strand from each DNA molecule goes to each of the two new cells. The strands are not the same, but in the new cells the strands rebuild their partners again, and the resulting double strands are identical with the double strands in the original cell. What happens is shown in schematic terms in the next column.

The DNA molecule is in fact self-reproducing; and this is a characteristic property of life. The whole of life is built on the ability of DNA to divide and re-make itself.

There is a last step still to be taken in going from one generation to the next. The hereditary material must be able to do something more than merely to reproduce itself. When it has reproduced itself, it must be able to foster and control the growth of the new, complete organism. How DNA does this is still a pioneering question. For the whole beautiful theory of the structure of DNA is very young; it was put forward by Francis Crick and James Watson in 1953. However, it seems clear that DNA is able to control the making of proteins, on which the development of the cells then depends. We can in fact actually see this happen, and can see chromosomes making proteins. We shall show recent pictures of this in Chapter 5. Thus the close likeness in structure between DNA and protein, each built from its own kinds of prefabricated building blocks, is not accidental. Molecules with this structure are of the very nature of life.

In summary, then, we have found the following points about living things. Chemically, they are no different from dead matter: they are made from the same atoms of hydrogen, of carbon, of oxygen and so on. What makes living things different is the arrangement of the atoms. The arrangement is more complex, but that is only a superficial way of putting it. The arrangement is built from bigger blocks of atoms, and these blocks—these prefabricated molecules—occur again and again in all living matter. The way living things are put together is not just chemistry; it is a form of architecture, and the units in the architecture of life are quite large. And some of these units must be capable of arrangements which can reproduce themselves, and act as template and copy at the same time.

Let us add two footnotes to this main theme. First, in all the units from which the architecture of life is built, carbon is the element which has the largest part. There is something about the way in which the atom of carbon can hold other atoms to it, and can form closed ring-like structures with them, which makes it central in living molecules. The units in which carbon is a skeleton are somehow stable and permanent. We cannot imagine life, we cannot conceive living things anywhere in the universe, built from units which are not based on the carbon atom.

And second, there is a strange quirk in the structure of living molecules. They are not symmetrical; they do not, like the crystal of salt, look the same from the right as from the left. It happens that all protein molecules are left-handed. That is, their structure is one-sided in the way in which a left-handed glove is one-sided. Living things do not contain the matching right-hand molecules. But the fact that protein molecules are left-handed is probably accidental. Certainly we can imagine living proteins in another world whose molecules would be all right-handed, like right-handed gloves. No, what seems to be fundamental is not one kind of asymmetry, either left or right, but asymmetry itself. Life is built up and kept going by unsymmetrical building blocks. Symmetry, uniformity are the states of the dead world; they are passive and, as it were, final. By contrast, life is active, disturbed and unfinished. Life resists the levelling processes of nature, which would produce right-handed and left-handed molecules at random and equally.

PART TWO—FOLLOWING INSTRUCTIONS

4

MACHINES THAT FOLLOW INSTRUCTIONS

Nature is not simply a collection of things. Everything in nature is in movement, and as time passes the things in it change from one state to another. When we observe the world, living or dead, what we look out for are the processes of change. Nature is dynamic; it does not consist of things but of processes.

The processes of change are everywhere, in dead as well as living nature. They are most evident, of course, in living things. Particularly we are conscious that living things reproduce themselves, in copies which go through the same cycle of change. We singled this out as the characteristic property of life in the last chapter.

In this chapter and the next, we shall ask how nature controls the sequence of steps in a living process. What makes an egg hatch out so that it becomes, day by day, a copy of the hen that laid it? And in particular, what controls the way in which the egg develops from day to day in an orderly sequence? How does nature build into the egg the instructions which cause it to develop in the right way, and not in some chaotic jumble?

These questions go very deep. If we are to answer them convincingly, we cannot simply appeal to vague natural forces. We must be able to present a mechanism for the orderly carrying out of instructions. That is, we must be able to imagine in our minds a machine which would do what nature does, at least in principle. We can only understand the mechanism behind living processes if we can see how a machine will do the same thing. For this reason, we shall begin in this chapter by looking at how an automatic machine receives its instructions and then carries them out.

In the past, in the Industrial Revolution of two hundred years ago, machines were no more than mechanical hands. But in recent years, changes have taken place in machines which are quite as important as the changes which made the Industrial Revolution.

In the Industrial Revolution, steam engines became the main source of power, and machines carried out the simple repetitive jobs previously done by hand. The machines were fast, but they were not flexible, and they needed constant supervision. The machines had to be controlled by a human operator.

The recent changes in machines are often called the second Industrial Revolution. The outstanding feature of this second Industrial Revolution is that control is also being made automatic. Many machines can now supervise themselves. This is the essential difference between the machines of the first and second Industrial Revolutions. The traditional machine of the past was ingenious, and it worked far faster than any hand weaver; but it needed constant attention from its operator. The new machine of today needs little supervision; for example, there are machines now that can cut out elaborate shapes from sheet metal automatically—they are not even restricted to any one shape.

Yet even the most versatile of modern automatic machines cannot look after itself all the time. It has to be given instructions. It may be able to do a lot of different jobs, but it has still to be told which to do at a particular time. The metal cutting machine, for example, can cut squares, circles, ovals, and more elaborate shapes; but it has still to be given an instruction for each shape.

Human beings can accept instructions in many different forms. If we want a table made to a particular design, we can show the cabinet maker another table like it. Or we can give him a model, or a photograph, or a set of drawings, or even a written description. The cabinet maker could follow any of these. A machine is much more selective. It is useless to show an automatic lathe a piece of metal like the one that we want turned. A lathe cannot copy a photograph either, or follow a blue-print. Automatic machines are made to take instructions in one form only.

Theoretically there is no reason why a lathe capable of following a blue-print could not be built. But for most uses, it would simply not be worth while. The apparatus for putting the information on the blue-print into a form acceptable to the control mechanism of the lathe would cost more than employing a man to do the job.

The reason why it is not usually useful to make a machine which will follow a blue-print is that the blue-print itself does not bear any relation to the way the machine will set about making the object shown on it. The instructions for a machine have to be divided into very simple steps, and the steps also have to be presented to the machine in the right order. The information in a blue-print is not in this form.

The best example of a series of simple steps set out in the right order is the punched tape. The instructions for many machines are in this form, shown in the picture below: nothing more than a sequence of holes in a tape. The pattern of holes is easy to

transform into the series of electrical impulses required by the electronic control systems.

Machines which carry out a co-ordinated series of steps can do remarkable things. For example, they can make calculations which at first sight seem very complex; and for this reason, these machines have earned the nickname of electronic brains. But in fact, when we look closely at what an electronic brain does, it turns out to be a sequence of very small and simple steps. In order to let an electronic brain, or any other automatic machine, carry out complex operations, we break up the operation into a long chain of simple steps, each of which is repeated many times.

For example, suppose that we want a machine to print for us a list of the squares of the whole numbers, like this:

$$1^2 = 1 \times 1 = 1,$$
$$2^2 = 2 \times 2 = 4,$$
$$3^2 = 3 \times 3 = 9,$$

and so on, up to, let us say,

$$999^2 = 999 \times 999 = 998{,}001$$

(Statisticians need such lists of squares, and they are printed in most books of Mathematical Tables.) Then it would be very wasteful to make a machine calculate each of these squares by a separate long multiplication. A much easier way is to make the machine simply carry out a series of additions, like this:

$$1 = 1 = 1^2,$$
$$1 + 3 = 4 = 2^2,$$
$$1 + 3 + 5 = 9 = 3^2,$$

and so on, up to

$$1 + 3 + 5 + 7 + \ldots + 1{,}997 = 998{,}001 = 999^2.$$

In this way, the machine needs to do nothing clever for itself. It needs only to go on adding up the sequence of odd numbers, $1 + 3 + 5 + 7 + \ldots$ and so on, one after the other.

The instructions for an electronic brain go into the machine as a string of holes, one after the other, on a long tape. There is nothing mysterious about the holes; they are a simple code for the numbers with which the machine deals. It is easier to make a machine recognise a set of holes than to make it read numbers; that is all.

But there is a deeper question here: Why do we put the instructions on a tape? The answer is that the machine always has to make a sequence of steps, one step after another. Therefore we arrange the instructions one after another, and the obvious way to do this is to string them out in the same order along a tape. Whatever the machine has to do, it must do in an order of time: the first step first, then the second step, and so on. And time has only a single dimension—the direction from the past into the future. There is no sideways in time, and no up-and-down. We may want the machine to make us a model which has extra dimensions of space—which has, that is, sideways and up-and-down as well as forwards. But since the machine will have to make the model in a sequence of steps in time, there is no point in giving it an array of instructions with more dimensions than one.

This picture shows an automatic typewriter following out some instructions that have been given on a punched tape. The instructions are not the sort of

the automatic typewriter is doing its normal job, the resemblance between instructions and final product is closer. A pattern of holes corresponds to each letter, just as a pattern of dots and dashes corresponds to each letter in the Morse code. But this resemblance is not necessary or usual in most machines. Most instructions are quite different from what is made when they are carried out.

This difference is very clear in the pictures below. On the left is a piece of video tape—the equivalent in television to magnetic tape in sound recording.

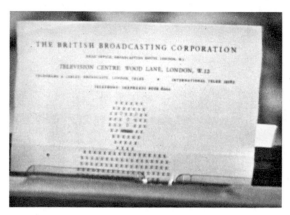

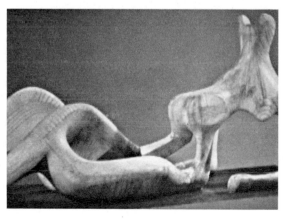

thing normally given to an electric typewriter. In response to them the typewriter is producing a rough silhouette of the human form. The point of the picture is to show that the instructions for a machine are usually quite unlike what the machine produces in response to them. On the one hand there is the paper tape with the instructions set out in a long string. On the other hand there is the two-dimensional shape the typewriter has made. When

Then we see it being put on the machine that reproduces it. Below is the picture that appears on the screen when what is recorded on the tape is transmitted. Here there is no resemblance between the

instruction (the tape) and the product (the picture on the screen) at all. The tape is not like a bit of film with tiny pictures on it. It is a pattern of magnetisation, just as the paper tape was a pattern of holes. The tape is the picture in coded form, but it is not like the pictures itself.

The idea of coding is central to this chapter. The word 'code' suggests at first a simple relation between the code and what is coded. But the word has a wider meaning than that. The pattern of magnetisation on a piece of video tape is as much a code for the picture as the Morse alphabet is a code for the printed alphabet.

What video tape, Morse code, punched tape and so on have in common is that they are all ways of recording and conveying information. Passing from information in one form to information in another is like translating from one language to another. Information in this context has an exact mathematical meaning. It is possible to assign a precise value to the amount of information in a picture or in a book. In going from video tape to a television picture, or from ordinary print to Morse code, the amount of information does not change.

What code is most useful for conveying information depends on each particular situation. New codes are invented to solve new problems of transmitting information as they arise. The Morse code for example was invented for sending information by telegraph. In the early telegraph systems it was difficult to distinguish between signals of different strengths. Therefore Morse devised a code in which it was only necessary to distinguish between signal and no signal, and between short and long pulses. A code with three different pulse lengths would have been perfectly feasible, or a code with only one kind of pulse. Morse chose his code for speed and ease of recognition, and it was a very good compromise in the circumstances.

In the same way the code used on magnetic tape was invented as a way of recording sound, and later television. Television itself is a way of coding the information in pictures in a form which can be broadcast. The signals from a television transmitter are not like the beam of light from a cinema projector. The television picture is coded in the form of modulations to a wave. And once again, a television receiver is a machine that gets its instructions in a long string. The information for making a whole picture does not arrive all at once. It is built up bit by bit as the spot flashes backwards and forwards across the screen.

We have been looking in this chapter at mechanisms which carry out an orderly process. Particularly we have looked at the way in which the shape of a thing is recorded so that it may be copied. The shape of a thing exists in the three dimensions of space—that is, forward-and-backward, sideways, and up-and-down. It is therefore surprising to find, as we have found, that the shape is best recorded and copied by instructions which have only one dimension—simply a string of marks or holes along a tape.

Usually we give instructions in a string because the machine that is to carry them out takes one step at a time. That is, the single dimension of the tape usually corresponds to the single dimension of time. But this is not the only reason for putting things on

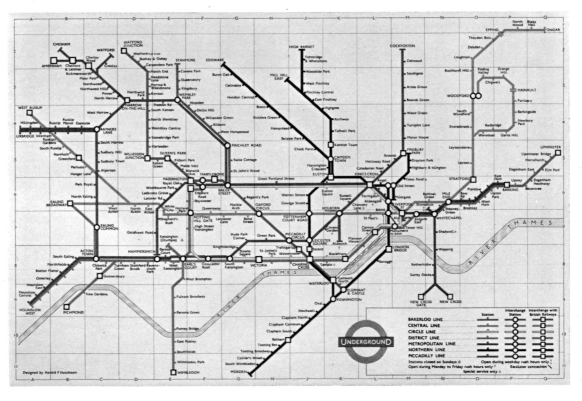

tape. The fact is that any configuration, however complex, can be unravelled as a series of paths which are most easily followed if we picture them as strings or tapes.

For example, an aerial photograph of London is highly complicated; and even if we simplify it as a

map, it still is immensely detailed. But if we want to get about London, we do not need anything so elaborate. If we want to get about London by Underground, all that we need is a string-like series of Underground lines to tell us how to get from one station to another. The map of the Underground system of London is in fact wildly distorted—in reality, the Underground system is not at all a series of straight lines. Yet this simplified map provides the right instructions just as well as if it were a correct picture in two dimensions (or in three dimensions, if we include the different depths of the different Underground lines).

Here is another map of the same kind. It represents the air corridors over Great Britain. It has been made to look very solid, but in fact the routes can be followed as instructions as simple as those of the London Underground system.

To round out this point, here finally is a map which shows the principle very elegantly. It is a map made by the natives of the Marshall Islands in the Pacific. The natives have not tried to record the exact disposition of the Islands. They have concentrated, just like the London Underground, on going from one station to another—from one island to another. Each island is represented by a shell, and the routes between the islands (and the winds and currents) are represented by bamboo rods. The bamboo rods, in fact, are the South Sea version of a tape of instructions.

5

MAPS OF INHERITANCE

The picture below illustrates how men tried long ago to explain the central puzzle in biology: How do living things reproduce themselves? How do they manage always to have young like themselves? Why do sheep have lambs, and cats have kittens?

In the Middle Ages, people actually believed that in the head of the sperm was a tiny man, a homunculus. The picture illustrates this belief, lingering as late as the seventeenth century. The idea of the homunculus seems rather absurd to us now, but it was not really so unreasonable in its time. A baby, after all, is like a small adult, and it seems to develop simply by getting bigger. What more natural than to assume that the same process goes on in the womb?

We know now of course that the homunculus theory is quite wrong. The complex yet constant pattern of inheritance is not handed on from generation to generation like an heirloom. Inheritance does not work by copying in the way that an artist copies from a model. The ovum that has just been entered and fertilized by a sperm does not look like a homunculus; it has to divide again and again and again, many thousands of times, before it reaches a recognisable shape. Only after a month does the embryo take on the basic shape in the first picture on the next page. The picture that follows it is after six weeks. In the next, the foetus is almost ready to be born; and in the last picture the baby is a few months old.

We are certainly not watching a tiny man gradually get bigger. The month-old embryo looks more like a fish or a tadpole than a man. In fact, young animals come to resemble their parents, not simply

by growing bigger, but by a process of development from something quite different.

In the last chapter we saw how, in response to a set of instructions, a machine can produce something utterly unlike the instructions themselves. A television picture on the screen is quite unlike the piece of video tape which records it. And the piece of video

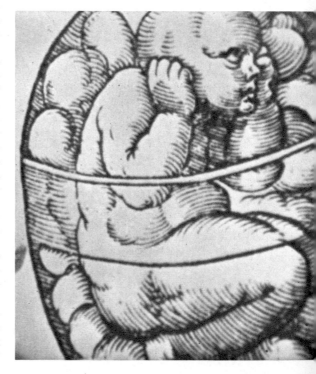

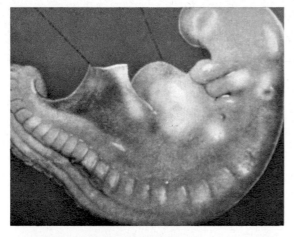 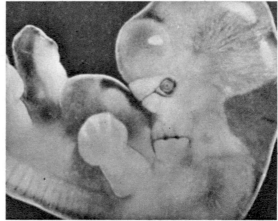

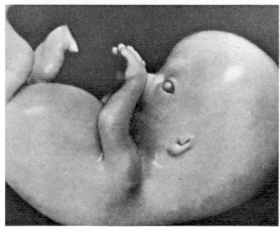 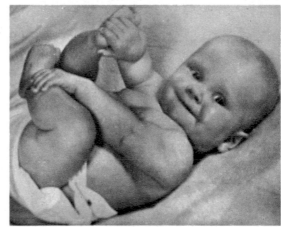

tape is a much truer analogy to what is in the sperm and the ovum than is the homunculus.

The sperm and the ovum carry sets of instructions that control the processes by which a single fertilised egg turns into an adult human being. What is passed on in inheritance is not a scale model of a man, but a coded message describing how the model is to be built. The instructions are in chemical form, and the processes they control are chemical reactions.

We saw in the last chapter that the instructions for many machines are in the form of a long string—a video tape, for example, or the punched tape for an automatic typewriter. The chemical instructions for inheritance in all forms of life also follow this arrangement. There is not a single string or tape, but several; just how many depends on the form of life. Whatever the form of life, the tapes are called chromosomes. In human beings, and in many other species, the chromosome tapes run in pairs; one tape of each pair comes from the father, and the other tape of the pair comes from the mother.

The pure chemical instructions which are strung out along the chromosomes are called genes. As an example of how genes act, let us take the control of the colour of a child's eyes. Eye colour is produced by different amounts of a pigment called melanin. Very little melanin in the iris of the eye causes it to look blue; more melanin causes the iris to look brown; and a great deal of melanin causes the iris to be black. Various genes control the amount of melanin that is laid down in the eyes, and in this way the genes control the colour of the child's eyes. Nearly every process in the body is controlled by the genes chemically, in the same way.

We have already seen in Chapter 3 how the hereditary instructions are passed on when a plant cell divides. The little black threads in the cell are the chromosomes; an identical set goes to each of the two new cells. Whenever a cell of any kind divides, a complete set of hereditary instructions goes to each of the daughter cells. This is the simplest type of biological reproduction. It is how primitive forms of life, such as bacteria and amoebae, multiply. More advanced forms of life reproduce sexually. Sexual reproduction is more complicated, and involves the combination of the chromosomes from both parents.

But even in the most advanced forms of life, cells in tissues like the skin and liver renew themselves by simple division.

This picture is a photograph, taken through the microscope, of the chromosomes in a human cell at the moment of division. These strands, only a few thousandths of an inch long, contain the complete instructions for building a human being and keeping him going.

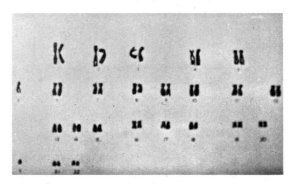

In the living cell the chromosomes are not arranged in any particular way. For purposes of classification, they have been arranged according to size in the picture below. One member of each pair

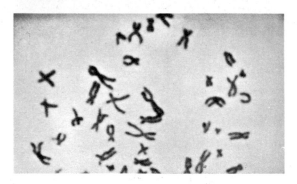

comes from the mother, the other from the father. In the agreed international system of classification for the human chromosomes each pair is given a number.

There are forty-six chromosomes in a normal human cell, but there are only twenty-two pairs, making forty-four paired chromosomes. The other two chromosomes, which do not always make a pair, are very important, since they determine the sex of the child. In females these two chromosomes do make a pair, and they are called X-chromosomes. Males however have only one X-chromosome; in place of the other, they have a very small Y-chromosome. The Y-chromosome does little except switch development as a whole to make a male as opposed to a female. The pictures that follow show these sex chromosomes in great enlargement. The picture at the top of the column shows the XX-chromosomes

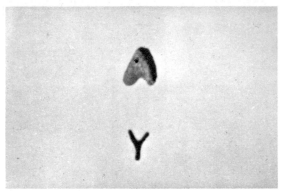

of a female. The one below it is the Y-chromosome of a male.

By examining the chromosomes in a human cell under a high-powered microscope it is possible to say whether the cell came from a male or a female, but normally nothing else can be inferred about an individual from the appearance of his chromosomes. The genes, the chemical instructions that make up the chromosomes, are far too small to be seen with even the most powerful microscope. So there is no prospect of deducing, say, the colour of someone's eyes by looking at his chromosomes.

However, some abnormalities are connected with changes in the chromosomes that are easy to see. This picture shows the chromosomes of an individual who has one chromosome too many. Instead of

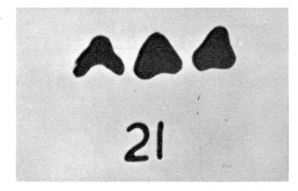

a pair of chromosomes at point number twenty-one, there are three. These chromosomes in fact come from a male mongol. Female mongols have a similar abnormality.

The photograph shows a group of mongol children. They have happy dispositions but they are al-

ways intellectually retarded. They get their name from the facial features that are characteristic of the condition.

Mongolism is directly due to the extra chromosome. It is as though an extra chapter had got bound into the book of hereditary instructions. Although each chapter makes perfectly good sense in itself, the extra one somehow interferes with the meaning of the others.

Why the extra chromosome, or extra chapter, should get bound into the book of instructions is not known. But it is easy enough to see how it happens. When the sperm and the ova are formed, portions of each pair of chromosomes are exchanged. It is at this stage of the division of a human cell that sometimes something goes wrong and gives the extra chromosome that causes mongolism. For some reason one chromosome goes to the wrong place, and the daughter cell that eventually forms on that side has one chromosome too many.

Mongolism is due to an extra chromosome, but abnormalities are much more commonly due to changes not in whole chromosomes but in the genes. If we use again the analogy of the book, then changes in the genes are equivalent to mistakes not in whole chapters but in single sentences. These changes in the genes are called mutations. At present, mutations can only be detected by their effects. It is not possible to see the individual genes that make up a human chromosome. A human chromosome that contains a mutated gene does not look abnormal in any way.

The geneticist's favourite experimental animal is the fruitfly. More is known about its heredity than

that of any other animal. The fruitfly is convenient because it has exceptionally large chromosomes (four pairs in all) that are easy to study in detail; because it breeds rapidly; and because the effects of the many mutations that it can undergo are easy to observe.

This picture shows a model of a fly with a mutation that has affected its eye. The condition is called bar-eye, and it obviously leads to much impaired sight. So much is known about the genetics of this fly that it is possible to pinpoint the position on the chromosome where the mutation has occurred.

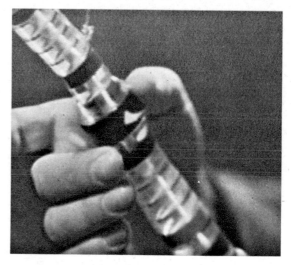

The place is marked on this greatly enlarged model of one of the fruitfly's four pairs of chromosomes. Though the position of the mutation is known, no actual change can be seen on the chromosome which reveals whether the mutation has taken place or not. There are visible marks on the large chromosomes of the fruitfly which seem to correspond to the position of individual genes—but changes in the genes have not been seen in a visible form. It is as if we were locating a fault in a radio set. The component that is giving the trouble looks usual enough;

it has to be identified by other tests. The chromosomes of the fruitfly have been mapped in such detail that the location of points affecting many parts of the fly are known.

These pictures show another example of a mutation in a fruitfly. This mutation affects the wing. On

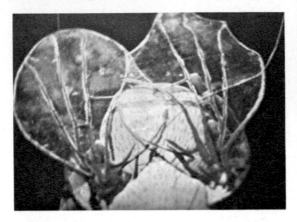

the model, only one wing is shown in the changed form; the other wing has been shown in the normal form, for comparison. (In reality, both wings would of course be affected by the mutation.) Again, the position of the mutated gene is known, and it is pointed to in the picture below.

The following pictures, taken only a year or so ago, take our knowledge of the chromosomes a stage further. They actually show a chromosome in action, producing chemicals in accordance with the instructions in the genes. In the top picture, the dark lines are the chromosomes; in this case they come from a newt. The lower picture is an enlargement of a small part of the top picture. The drop-like bodies are the chemicals being pushed out by the chromosomes. These pictures take us a long way beyond the theorising of Gregor Mendel who, from his experiments with garden peas, laid the foundations of modern genetics less than a hundred years ago.

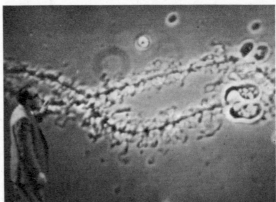

Some progress has also been made in mapping the human chromosomes. Since human populations cannot be studied under laboratory conditions, however, a good deal less is known about human chromosomes than about the chromosomes of the fruitfly. The longevity of humans is another difficulty, and human geneticists have to rely greatly on pedigrees for their material.

The first problem in mapping one chromosome of any species is to find a marker—a gene that controls some clearly recognisable characteristic. Other characteristics which are passed on from generation to generation with the marker can thus be assumed to be controlled by genes on the same chromosome. In this way genes can be grouped according to the chromosomes on which they are found.

It is still difficult to assign groups of genes to particular human chromosomes—to say, for example, that such and such a group of human genes belongs to chromosome number ten. We are in the state of having maps which only cover parts of a group of islands, and we do not know which island is which. Each chromosome is an island, and though we sometimes have maps of parts of an island, we do not know which island the parts belong to.

The best mapped human chromosome is the X-chromosome. This is no coincidence; obviously the sex chromosome can be identified, because sex itself is an obvious marker. There are some characteristics that appear most often, or only, in males, yet which the pedigree shows to have been transmitted by the female parent. Now males have only a single X-chromosome, which dominates their sexual make-up; and they must receive this X-chromosome from their mother. These characteristics must therefore be controlled by genes on the X-chromosome. So sex is a marker that enables genes to be assigned to a chromosome, the X-chromosome, that can actually be indentified under the microscope.

The most striking of all genetically transmitted characteristics that appear in one sex only is haemophilia—the condition in which the blood will not clot. A gene on the X-chromosome is concerned in blood clotting, and if this gene mutates, so that it gives the wrong instruction, the clotting of the blood is impeded.

Haemophilia appears only in males. The reason that females are not affected is this. The female has two X-chromosomes, one from each parent. Since haemophilia is so rare, it is most unlikely that both X-chromosomes will carry the defective gene. So women carriers of haemophilia have the gene giving the wrong instruction about blood clotting on only one X-chromosome. On the other X-chromosome, in the equivalent position, there will be a normal blood clotting gene giving the right instruction. This normal gene dominates or masks the effect of the other.

In males, the situation is different. Instead of a second X-chromosome they have a Y-chromosome. The Y-chromosome does not carry instructions about blood clotting, and so the abnormal gene on the X-chromosome is able to exert its effect.

This diagram is a family tree of the most famous carrier of haemophilia in history—Queen Victoria. A solid circle surrounded by a circle indicates a female carrier; solid squares indicate actual haemophilics, all of course males. Queen Victoria's three daughters were all carriers, but her son, Edward VII was not a haemophilic. A female carrier of haemophilia has two X-chromosomes, only one of which contains the abnormal gene, so she does not necessarily pass it on to all her children. Haemophilia first appeared in Queen Victoria's grandchildren. Its appearance in her great-grandchild, the Tsarevich, was of more than medical importance, since it was one of the reasons for Rasputin's influence at the Russian court at the time of the first World War.

Haemophilia is easy to detect and to trace from generation to generation; and since it is linked with sex, it is easy to assign the gene to a particular chromosome. Usually mapping the human chromosomes is very much more difficult. However, pro-

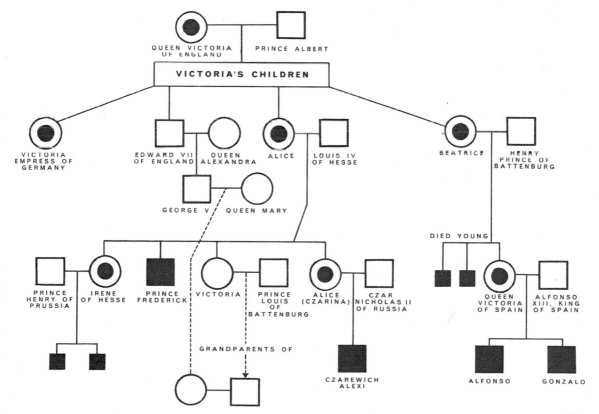

gress has been made in recent years in grouping sets of different characteristics together, even when it is not possible to say on which chromosome the genes responsible for a group of characteristics belong.

In this research, the various human blood groups have been most useful as markers. For example, there is a gene (or a set of genes) which causes the nails and kneecaps of a child to be smaller than usual. This gene (or set of genes) has been shown to be on the same chromosome as the genes of the ABO blood group system. Similarly, the genes of the Rhesus blood group have been shown to be on the same chromosome as the genes which give rise to the formation of red blood cells which are oval in shape, and which are found in some people instead of the normal round blood cells. By detecting and tracing such slight abnormalities, the gaps on the map of the human chromosomes are gradually being filled in. There are likely to be big advances here in the next few years.

Let us summarise what we have found in this chapter and the last. Nature passes the pattern of life from generation to generation very much as we would pass a pattern to a machine. We would give a machine the pattern, not as a solid model, but as a set of instructions strung out along a tape. In the same way, the fertilised egg carries the pattern of the child to be, not as a solid model, but as instructions on a series of tapes—on the forty-six human chromosomes. The fertilised egg has received these chromosomes in pairs, taking one of each pair from the father and one from the mother.

Each chromosome carries a large array of instructions—so large that we have referred to each chromosome as a book of instructions. The individual instructions on each chromosome are the genes and they are, as it were, sentences which tell the body what chemicals to produce. (We have seen a striking picture of these chemicals being produced at various points along the chromosome.) We also know what the genes are made of: they are made of different forms of the basic material of life, De-oxy-ribo-Nucleic Acid, or DNA for short, which we have already met in Chapter 3. Thus the code in which nature prints her instructions consists of words which are forms of DNA.

We saw in Chapter 3 that DNA itself is always built up from the same four basic units. These four units are the letters of the alphabet in which nature prints the whole pattern of heredity. And these four letters are the same in all living things—in a bacterium and in a rose just as in a child. Every form of life reproduces itself, from generation to generation, by handing on instructions which are printed from the same four letters, the same four fundamental chemical molecules. This is a powerful argument for thinking that all life on earth has a single, common origin.

6

THE LOGIC OF SPACE

A child exists, at any moment, in all the three dimensions of space—it has height, breadth and thickness. Yet the instructions which cause the child to have its own features, a high forehead, a broad grin, a stubby nose—the instructions for all these came from the parents as a set of strings with only one dimension. And these strings, the forty-six human chromosomes, give rise to all those subtle patterns which make one child recognisably like another, and yet make each one in some way different from the others.

There was a time in the Middle Ages when men thought that the child was a fully formed figure in three dimensions from the instant of its conception. At that time, the shapes of things were thought of very simply. Now we see that shape is a much more delicate idea, and that we must not think of it as something fixed and rigid. We realise that the space of three solid dimensions in which we move every day is not the only kind of space. Our picture of the development of things, and particularly of living things, is a picture in which the parts do not all grow in the same fixed way. We have something to learn about the structure of things, and about the relation of shape to structure, by thinking about the nature of space itself. Earlier chapters of this book have already stressed the importance of architecture —of the way things are put together. This chapter is concerned with the shapes of things as a whole: with space.

The mathematical study of shapes is called topology. It is part of the geometrical side of math-

ematics, which is quite different from the arithmetical side. In many ways, modern topology is as characteristic of our way of looking at the world as Euclidean geometry was of the Greek picture of the world. Topology deals with distortions and manipulations of space; Greek geometry dealt with fixed ideal shapes.

The shapes of most things, particularly man-made things, are not arbitrary. They are closely related to function. The objects in the picture below and those over the page show this clearly. Below is a ship's propeller. Its function is to push the water aside, and this is expressed in the twist and curve of the blades.

Similarly, the lines of the ploughshare in the picture above show that it is meant for pushing earth aside. The delta wing, top right, is a more modern example, and here the shape is clearly designed to cut through the air at speed. Cleaving the water, the earth, the air—these are the functions which are plainly expressed in these three shapes. The relationship between shape and function is better recognised today than at any time in man's history. We even accept a close connection between shape and function as a criterion of merit in the design of man-made things.

The clover-leaf crossing in the next picture is interesting because it uses the manipulation of space in an ingenious way to solve a particular problem—getting from one traffic stream to another without crossing a third. There is only a single road surface in the clover-leaf crossing—that is, one can get from any point on it to any other point without leaving the road. Yet the way the road surface is arranged in space—its shape—avoids the disorder of intersecting traffic streams. The clover-leaf crossing is a clever piece of topology.

In the clover-leaf crossing, space is manipulated in the interests of traffic engineering. The next picture below it shows an example of space manipulated for reasons that are not purely practical. It is a piece of sculpture by Henry Moore. The work by Henry Moore does not look like any one woman, and indeed bears little direct relation to reality; yet we recognise it at once as a female form. Perhaps our acceptance of distortion in art today has something to do with our familiarity with distortion in the world around us. Things which stretch, contract, change their shape, and can be taken to pieces are very much part of our everyday life in the twentieth century.

A sculptor can make any distortions that suit his purpose, but the distortions allowed in topology

have to follow a strict rule. In topology, neighbouring points must remain neighbours. That is, a topological figure may be stretched, squeezed, and twisted, just like a length of rubber. But it must not be cut in any way, and it must not be joined together in any way.

This rule underlies many well-known topological puzzles. In the puzzle shown in the pictures below are two people joined together by two pieces of string. Each starts with a piece of string knotted to both wrists, and the two loops formed by these two strings are interlaced like two links of a chain. The two people are asked to separate. No cutting of the string and no untying of knots is allowed, for either of these actions would break the topological

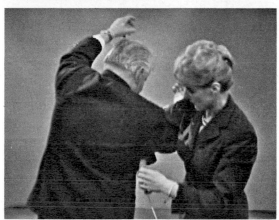

rule that neighbouring points must remain neighbours.

Of course if the two loops really were joined like links of a chain there would be no getting apart; as the pictures show, mere twisting and turning gets the couple nowhere. But a closer analysis shows us that the loops are not closed. They are in effect open at each wrist; and therefore the couple can get apart by passing, say, the man's loop under the string round the woman's wrist, and then over her hand.

The puzzle of the key in the lock, tied to a girl by a loop of string, is of the same kind. The pictures above illustrate what the problem is.

The girl is about to be tied solidly by both wrists to the two ends of a string which has been looped double through a fixed key. How does she get the string off the key? The reader is left to solve this problem for himself.

In the elastic space of topology and of these puzzles, it might seem that all shapes are alike. A rubber ball can be turned into a cube, and a rubber bust of Newton into a bust of Einstein, without breaking the rule. But our first impression is wrong; all shapes are not really equivalent. Even in topology there are fundamentally different shapes which cannot be turned into one another. The two most obviously different shapes are the ball and the ring. A solid ball can be turned into a solid cylinder without breaking the connection between neighbouring points, or making new connections. But to turn the cylinder into a ring, new connections would have to be made between the two flat ends of the cylinder. This would join points which were not neighbours before, and the rule of topology does not allow this. So the ball and the ring are basically different shapes.

The world we live on is of course a ball, but many of the tests we use to show that it is round would apply just as well if it were a ring and not a ball. For example, ships would disappear over the horizon on a ring just as they do on a sphere.

How can we show that the earth is a sphere and not a ring? In the picture below, the Mediterranean countries are shown arranged on a ring, and below that is an ordinary globe for comparison. How do we know the globe is right, and the ring is wrong? That is, how can we test that there is not a hole right through the earth in the Mediterranean or one of the other seas?

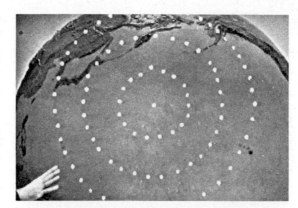

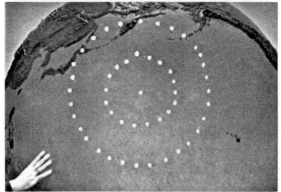

The tests examine the kind of path that it is possible to take on the different kinds of world. Consider a path circumnavigating the globe—the outermost path on the first picture above. Imagine this path as a rubber band which is slipped a little way up the globe to the next smaller path. If this operation is repeated often enough the path will shrink to a single point, as in the last picture of the set, on the next page. This is true for any closed path on the globe. It does not matter whether it goes round the equator, or across the poles, or by way of Tierra del Fuego and Kamchatka—any closed path in a sphere can be shrunk to a point.

Now consider the equivalent closed paths on the

ring-shaped world. Here, by contrast, there are some closed paths that cannot be shrunk to a point. A path right round the ring, for example, cannot be shrunk indefinitely; the space in the middle of the ring gets in the way, and no more shrinking of the path is possible.

This, then, is a fundamental way of distinguishing between a sphere-shaped space and a ring-shaped space. On a sphere, every closed path can be shrunk to a point. On a ring, some closed paths cannot be shrunk to a point. All closed paths on earth can be shrunk to a point; but an inhabitant of the rings of Saturn could follow paths that could not be shrunk to a point. The Greeks, sailing round the shores of the Mediterranean but not crossing from side to side, might have been living on a ring-shaped world for all they knew from their voyages.

This fundamental difference can be put in another way. If we cut along a closed path on a sphere, the surface of the sphere will fall into two parts. But when we cut along some closed paths on a ring (paths which cannot be shrunk to a point) the surface of the ring remains in one piece.

Our lives are full of examples of these two different topological shapes: bolts and nuts, for example, and rods and tubes. The most interesting example of the two shapes, however, comes from biology. Rings and spheres have a real evolutionary significance, and the transition from one to the other is a vital step on the evolutionary ladder that leads from the amoeba to man. Essentially, all the higher animals—roughly everything on the evolutionary scale above the worm —are rings. The animals below the worm are essentially spheres.

Let me explain what is meant by this strange statement. The basic difference appears in the way that the animals pass food through themselves. All animals have to take in food from their surroundings, extract what they need from it, and get rid of the waste products. The higher animals do so by taking in their food at one end of a tube, absorbing nourishment as it passes down the tube, and discharging the waste products at the other end of the tube. And a tube, of course, is an example of the ring-shaped space. A ring can be turned into a tube simply by stretching it. But a sphere cannot be turned into a tube without breaking the rule of topology, as we have seen.

Now contrast the lower animals. Consider the beautiful sea-anemones seen below. If I pick one of them up as in the pictures, it becomes clear at once that it works in an entirely different way. It takes in its food and throws out the waste products through the same orifice. The sea-anemone has only one opening, as the pictures show. When the sac has something in it, the tentacles close over the top, but the edges at the top do not join up. This is as if the draw-string at the top of a bag were being pulled tight. When the food has been absorbed, the draw-string is loosened again, the waste thrown out, and the animal is ready to take in another batch of food.

Thus the sea-anemone is a sphere, in the topological sense. That is, its shape can be obtained by distorting a sphere, without breaking the topological rule. It has the shape one gets by squeezing a hollow rubber ball until one side becomes concave and it turns into a cup. So the sea-anemone has a fundamentally different shape from the higher animals, and this reflects the fundamentally different way in which it manipulates its food.

All forms of life start as single cells, so even the higher animals begin their existence as spheres. The point where the little ball of cells turns into a ring is a very important step in the development of the embryo. The process starts with the ball turning into a cup, and then at the point of contact between the two layers of cells, an opening appears. This breaks a topological rule, and the sphere becomes a ring. Thus, in the evolution of the higher animals, a new manipulation of space appears when the embryo folds into a ring.

The examples of topology that we have given so far have been concerned with the way shapes can be

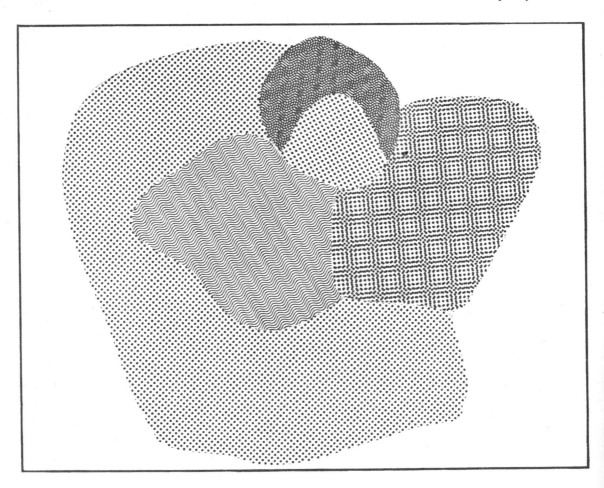

distorted. This is not the only concern of topology. Topology is concerned with all the relations within different kinds of spaces and shapes. So, as a final example, here is rather a different problem in topology.

Everyone knows that atlases are printed in four colours. For experience has shown that four colours are enough to ensure that no two countries with a common boundary need have the same colour. The last picture shows this with four different patterns in place of four colours. Here the fifth country—the largest shape—does not touch the country marked with dots, and therefore it can be marked with dots also.

So, in general, the fifth of five interlocking shapes can never touch more than three of the others. We therefore believe that any flat map can be coloured with four colours, in such a way that no two countries with a common boundary have the same colour. In practice, this theorem of topology has been known for centuries. And mathematicians have been trying to prove it logically for more than a hundred years. Yet no one has ever produced a proof without some logical flaw. So it remains possible that maps exist which need five colours; but no one has ever found one.

There is an interesting footnote to this theorem. A map on a sphere needs the same number of colours as a flat map—four, we believe. But a map on a ring can need more colours. We can prove logically, and we can show by actual examples, that a map on a ring can need as many as seven colours.

In this book, we have many examples of how the insight that scientific observation gives us reveals new relations between things and ideas. Topology is another such example. It is the study of the relations within the variety of shapes and forms. Looked at topologically, the bewildering array of shapes in the natural and man-made worlds can be reduced to an order. This order is something more than a mere convenience of classification. In the biological example we saw that the fundamental shapes, the ring and the sphere, are of great significance in evolution, dividing the higher from the lower animals. Superficially there is not much connection between nuts and bolts on the one hand, and bacteria and mammals on the other. Yet topology reveals just such subtle and interesting connections.

PART THREE—ORDER AND DISORDER

7

UNITS OF MATTER AND ENERGY

We have looked at the way that matter is put together already, in several chapters. Each time we have taken for granted what is now common knowledge, namely, that all matter is built up from tiny separate particles. At one time, the smallest particles were thought to be atoms, and therefore the theory that matter is put together in this way is still called an atomic theory. (Today it would no doubt be better, but more pedantic, to call it a particulate theory.)

Of course it is not at all obvious that matter is atomic or particulate. On the contrary, the bare evidence of the eye and hand suggests quite the opposite—suggests that matter is made of some continuous stuff. And in fact, the simple theories that men first made for themselves treated matter as if it were formed out of a continuous jelly.

So there have been two kinds of theories about

matter: those which have treated it as continuous, and those which have treated it as atomic. This state of affairs applies not only to matter, but to other phenomena of nature. In particular, there have been two kinds of theory about energy (for example, about light). The simple first theory, which once seemed obvious to everyone, was that energy is continuous. Only since 1900 have we discovered that this is not so, and that energy also comes in definite particles. This chapter shows how we know that energy is not continuous but is particulate.

In order to make the reasoning clear, I will begin by looking again at the way that matter appears to us. To the naked senses, the atomic theory of matter seems most unlikely. Liquids in particular just do not appear to be made of hard particles. And sometimes

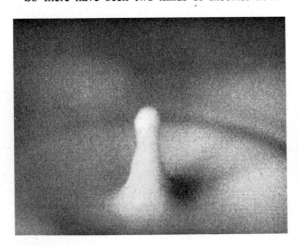

the tests which might be expected to give us more insight into the nature of things seem at first to point in the wrong direction. For example, should not an enlarged and slow-motion film of a liquid show the atoms? We might hope so, but we would be disappointed. In fact, look at these two pictures taken when a drop of milk has fallen into a pool of milk. The sharp, sudden splash looks more continuous here, not less; it is revealed as a gently spreading wave, arching drops, smooth shapes. Smoothly (and surprisingly) a round drop detaches itself from the top of the splash. These do not seem to be the forms that matter should take if it is made up of atoms.

The reason for the apparent contradiction here is that atoms are so small. The atomic nature of matter is not obvious in the things we do and see on the normal scale of life. Yet an everyday example can show us that collections of particles sometimes look and behave like fluids: the sand flowing through the tiny hole in an hour-glass runs and looks like a liquid. Grains of sand are big enough for us to see. With particles of the size of atoms the effect is enormously greater.

Even with a microscope we have no hope of seeing atoms. But with a microscope it is possible to see some of the effects of motion on an atomic scale. Atoms and molecules are constantly in movement, and we can watch the traces of this movement.

The first observation of this kind was made by the English botanist Robert Brown nearly one hundred and fifty years ago. Brown was watching pollen grains floating on the surface of water, and he noticed that they were never at rest. All the time the grains were moving about the surface in zig-zag paths, darting to and fro. Brown could not explain what he saw. Now we know that the Brownian movement (as it is called) is caused by the water molecules knocking the pollen grains about. Eighty years later, Albert Einstein explained, on the basis of the atomic theory, that particles floating on the surface of a liquid would be knocked about by the motion of the liquid molecules. Oddly enough, Einstein had not at the time heard of Brown's observations. In the same way, tobacco smoke trembles because the grains in it are bounced about by the molecules of the air.

The atomic theory of matter has been known since Greek times. The evidence for it has steadily accumulated in the last century and in this. There have been a few surprises, but none that called for any fundamental change of view. It was unexpected, for example, that atoms themselves would have a structure; yet this turned out to be easy to fit into the general framework of the atomic theory.

In 1900, however, the German physicist Max Planck made a discovery about the nature of energy that shook physics to its foundations. He showed that energy is not continuous, but comes in minute packets which behave in many ways like particles.

Particulate theories of energy were not wholly new. Isaac Newton, for example, had believed that light consists in some sense of particles. But at the end of the last century, such ideas were very much in the background. The idea of perfectly smooth waves dominated people's thinking, and the possibility of energy in packets hardly crossed anyone's mind. Planck's theory, and its subsequent amplification by Einstein, revolutionised physics.

Even today some of its implications are still startling. Suppose we have a light shining on a screen, and between the light and the screen we put a dark filter. Then the intensity of the light reaching the screen is of course reduced. By inserting more and more filters, we can reduce the intensity further and further. Nineteenth century physics thought that with suitable filters we can reduce the intensity evenly and smoothly, as low as we like. Now we know that this is not so. Since light energy comes in packets, the intensity can only be reduced in steps, a packet at a time. At very low intensities, the screen will not be illuminated evenly. Instead, packets of light will arrive at different parts of the screen at different times.

When Einstein wrote his famous paper on light in 1905, he understood this, but he could not demonstrate it. Nowadays, with the apparatus shown in the following pictures, the individual packets of light can actually be seen hitting the screen. At the business end of the apparatus is a tube closed at one end by a cap with a tiny hole in it. At the other end of the

tube is a screen. Behind the screen is a modern device, which Einstein did not have, for amplifying the faint flashes of light as the packets arrive. Whenever a packet of light hits the screen, the recording spot jumps across the scale, as the next picture shows.

In a brightly lit room so many packets of light get through the tiny hole that the recording spot remains at the end of the scale all the time. As the lights are dimmed, the recording spot starts to jerk about. It

D

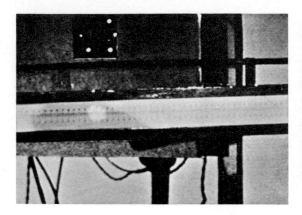

kicks when a packet of light strikes the screen; so when the total light is dim enough, individual packets can be detected as they reach the screen. Thus we can actually see that they arrive not in a steady stream but in sporadic bursts, at random.

Max Planck called a packet of energy a quantum, and the name has remained. His theory that energy is particulate is therefore called the quantum theory. Einstein coined a special name for the quantum of light energy: he called it an arrow of light. Alas, his vivid name has not remained in use. A special name for the quantum of light is used, but it is less picturesque; the quantum of light is now called a photon.

The next series of pictures demonstrates the grainy, particulate nature of light in a more subtle way. At first sight, there is nothing here to show single quanta of light, single photons. The pictures seem at first sight too ordinary for that. The first is part of an aerial photograph of London. A small piece of it has been marked out in white and it is just possible to see that this is a car park with some buildings on it.

In the second picture the car park has been enlarged. The rough shape of buildings and cars is clearer, but the detail is not. On the contrary, the enlargement has blurred the detail. The small piece that has been marked out in this picture is only just recognisable.

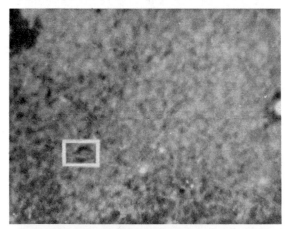

In the third picture the detail can no longer be recognised, and the picture has lost its overall meaning. A smaller patch, which has been squared off in white, is barely recognisable as a pool of water. And when this is enlarged—the fourth picture—there is no detail at all. It consists now of patches of black and white, with no gradation between them. It is as if the picture had become coarse—as coarse as the grain of the photographic film.

The fifth and final enlargement shows that this is indeed so: the grain of the photograph is all that can be distinguished now. The grain consists of a jigsaw

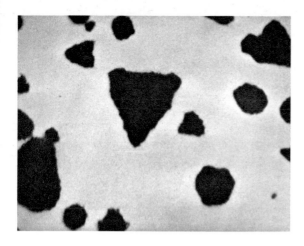

parts that respond directly to light. When an arrow of light, a photon, strikes one of the long thin receptors, called rods, the pigment within the rod bleaches momentarily and sends a tiny impulse to the optic nerve. The blunt cigar-shaped objects are another type of receptor called cones, which behave in the same way. They are responsible for vision in bright light, and for our ability to see colours.

There are literally millions of receptors in the human eye, and they respond individually to single photons. The impulses from all of them pass to the brain through the optic nerve, and the brain integrates them into the picture we see. The second picture, the photograph below, taken through an ophthalmoscope, shows the ending of the optic nerve inside the eye. The actual nerve ending is the white spot where the blood vessels meet. It is less than a tenth of an inch across.

The following picture shows a model of the human eye. On the next page the model is opened out. The dark lines are blood vessels, the interruption in the outer layers on the right is the ending of the optic nerve. Next is shown part of the same model, on a larger scale. Here the thin inside layer of the eye's outer casing is the retina, the light-sensitive surface on which are the rods and cones. In each eye there are about a hundred million rods and

of individual crystals of silver bromide. And this picture shows that it is a jigsaw of blacks and whites—there are no greys. What greys there were in the aerial photograph are now seen to be average effects, made up of some black and some white crystals. Because matter consists of individual grains, because the photographic film consists of individual crystals, every shade is produced by a jigsaw in which the pieces are either pure black or pure white.

But it is not only matter that is grainy. The fifth picture proves that light also comes in single units. For it is clear that either the light strikes a crystal of silver bromide and turns it black, or it misses the crystal completely and leaves it white. There is no in-between effect; there is no half-unit of light which can turn a crystal to some shade of half-black. A single crystal is either struck, or it is not struck. Therefore what strikes the crystal must be a single unit of light, a single quantity of energy which cannot be divided into smaller parts. A crystal has either been struck by one quantum of light, one photon, or by none. Einstein's picturesque name says it vividly: the light strikes the photographic plate as a shower of single arrows.

Human vision depends on these arrows of light, and our eyes are beautifully adjusted to them. The picture below—also the first of a series of five pictures—is a diagram of the receptors in the eye—the

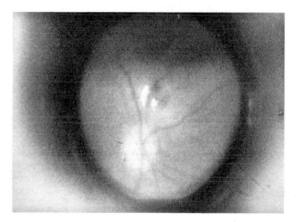

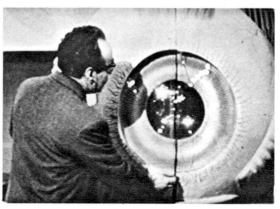

51

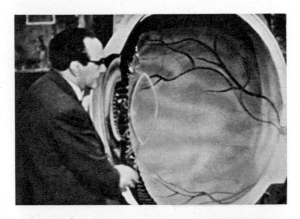

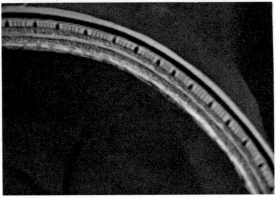

six million cones—well over a hundred million individual receptors. Each receptor can respond to a single photon of light. The brain has to integrate the impulses from all of them.

The series of pictures on the right hand page show a schematic model which imitates the state of affairs in a small part of the retina: a part containing only about a thousand receptors. In the model, each receptor is imitated by a little bulb. A bulb flashing on for a moment imitates a receptor being struck by a photon. The first two pictures are equivalent to the state of affairs when the eye is receiving fairly bright light. Most of the receptors are being struck by photons, but by no means all of them. Notice that the pattern is random; the photons do not arrive regularly. It is the sort of pattern that one would get by throwing a handful of sand at a flypaper; the grains would stick in patches here and there, not in an orderly array.

Of course, one picture of the model with flashing lights imitates the state of affairs in the eye at one instant only. The pattern is changing all the time. If the brightness of the light remains constant, the proportion of receptors that are being struck at any one moment does not change. But it is not the same individual receptors that are being struck and stim-

ulated. We have given two pictures of the model in order to show the pattern of stimulation changing while the intensity of illumination remains the same.

In the third picture, a shape (roughly like the letter C) has been put in front of the model. We can see that the outline of the shape remains sharp, even though the pattern of receptors which are being struck is changing from picture to picture. At this level of illumination, shapes remain distinct, in spite of the particulate structure both of the retina and of the light which strikes it.

Things are different, however, when the level of illumination is reduced. The next picture shows how the receptors on the retina behave when the eye is receiving a good deal less light than in the first three. Again there is a random pattern. Individual receptors are stimulated as before. But they are stimulated less often. The proportion of them that is being stimulated at any time is lower. There are more areas at any one time that are not being struck by arrows of light. And because there are more dark areas, the sharp outline of the shape is lost. Its position is still evident, but its width cannot be judged accurately any more.

The last two pictures take things two stages further. The level of illumination is being taken lower and lower; fewer and fewer of the receptors in the model are flashing at any one moment. Now the shape of the C in front of the screen and even its position is no longer clear. The dark areas are now so large that they are comparable in size with the shape itself. So the shape gets lost; there are just not enough receptors stimulated at any one time to define it. True, by putting together a great many single pictures of this kind, it would be possible to work out where the shape is. That is, if we waited long enough, all the receptors not obscured by the shape would flash sooner or later. But the brain is not able to integrate the patterns it receives over such long periods. It cannot remember which receptors have been stimulated for more than a very short time.

Thus the eye itself is the most beautiful proof of the quantum theory. It is filled with millions of individual receptors, precisely in order to respond to the shower of individual photons. Only so can we explain, as we have just seen, why we lose the outline of things in dim light. We have all noticed this; when the level of illumination is low, at dusk for example, shapes lose their sharpness and merge into one another. If light were not grainy, if it were smooth and continuous, the contrast between light and dark would be reduced in a dim light, but outlines would not be affected. The loss of sharp outline is a direct effect of the interaction between single photons of light and single receptors. In fact, only the quantum

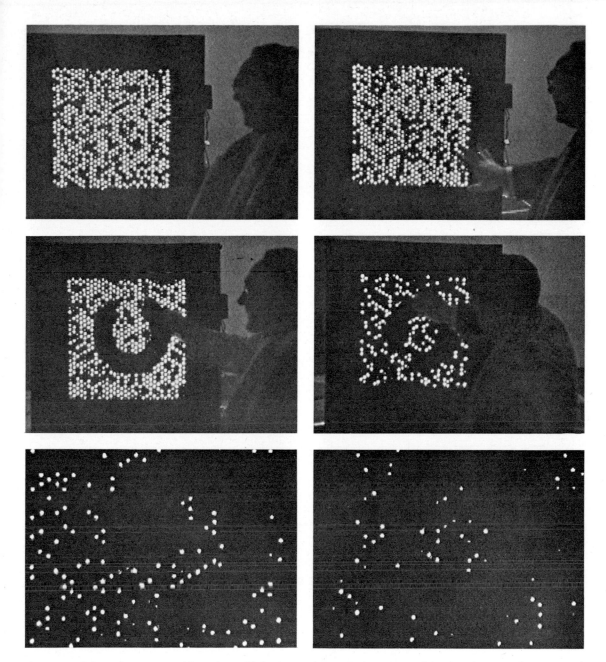

theory explains why we see things in twilight less sharply than in daylight.

The eye is of course only part of our visual apparatus. The brain is just as important. It is the brain that turns the nerve impulses from the receptors on the retina, the rods and cones, into a picture. In Chapter 4 we saw how important codes are in transmitting information. The eye turns its visual information into a code for the brain. It transforms the pattern of light and shade and colour on the retina into a code of electrical impulses, which pass along the optic nerve to the brain. Information

from all the senses, sight, hearing, touch, taste and smell, reaches the brain in this form, as a code of electrical dots and dashes.

This chapter started with contradictions: in appearance, matter and energy are continuous, yet in underlying structure they are both particulate. On one hand, the appearances: gently rounded drops of milk, smooth waves, regularity. On the other hand, the facts behind the appearances: atoms of matter, quanta of energy, jostling about in a way which is full of randomness, irregularity and unpredictability.

But the examples have shown that there is no real contradiction. If the particles of matter and the pockets of energy are small enough, and there are enough of them, their total behaves as though it were continuous.

The apparatus in these pictures shows the effect of large numbers particularly well; it was invented by the great statistician Francis Galton. When pollen grains are thrown in through the hole at the top, they can fall into any of the compartments at the bottom of the box. If we throw in a small number of grains, they distribute themselves between the different compartments at random. But as we throw in more and more grains, the random arrangement takes on a regular shape. A large number of grains arranges itself, by simple probability, in the shape of a wave, as in the picture on the right. Just so a large number of atoms pushed aside on the surface of a pool takes on the shape of a wave. And just so also a large number of photons of light behaves collectively like a wave.

The individual behaviour of atoms or of quanta is random, irregular, unpredictable. But the collective outcome of their behaviour is regular and predictable. The study of the predictable outcome of large numbers of individually unpredictable events is called statistics, and statistics is the subject of the next chapter.

8

THE IDEA OF STATISTICS

We ended the last chapter with a simple experiment: we dropped pollen grains into a box which was divided into compartments. In such an arrangement, it is not possible to say in advance where any individual grain will fall. Yet the shape which the whole heap of grains will take up is quite predictable. The same is true of a heap of atoms, and even of the flow of light. Single events are often unpredictable, but in large numbers the events fall into a regular order. This is the idea of statistics.

The idea of statistics applies, for example, to the letters on this page. If you close your eyes and stick a pin into the paper, it is impossible to predict what will be the nearest letter to the pin. But if you do the same thing a great many times, then predictions can be made about the result. We can say with assurance, for example, that the nearest letter to the pin will more often be *E* than any other letter—simply because *E* is the commonest letter in English. In fact, if we make a table of the number of times that each letter occurs on a given page of this book, we shall find that the tables are roughly the same for one page as for another. They will all be fairly close to this table, which gives the approximate frequency of the various letters in ordinary written English.

E	13%	T	9%	A and O	8%	
N and I	7%	S and R	6%	H	5%	
L and D	4%	C, U and F	3%	M, P, W and Y	2%	
B, G and V	1%	K, Q, X, J and Z	less than $\frac{1}{2}$%			

There will, however, always be fluctuations round the frequencies listed in this table, because the table is made up of averages for very large numbers. And the fluctuations will be larger, the shorter the passage which we are counting. A page of this book contains about 1,000 letters, and the percentages of the different letters will be close to the numbers in this table, but they will not be exactly the same. (For example, some pages in this book do not contain the letter *V* at all.) If we take a passage much shorter than 1,000 letters, we must expect to meet quite wide departures from the average.

Let us try this on a practical example and, to make the trial more interesting, let us put it in the form of a problem. Here is a classical passage in English literature which is less than 500 letters long. It is written in a simple substitution code—that is, each letter in the original has been replaced by one letter. As is usual in codes, we are not told where the divisions between one word and the next come; that is, all the words have been run together. In order to make it easier to count and study the sequence of letters, a gap has been left every five letters. (This is usual in coded passages, and is done simply to rest the eye—the gaps have no other meaning.) Each line of twenty letters is to be read straight across the page, and the passage reads as follows:

We begin with a count. The 419 letters occur the following numbers of times.

OAMRA	DYAOO	AMROX	HOCNO
XRFGR	NOCAY	LXROX	RDOCN
YAMBR	DCYOX	RTCYW	OANGP
PRDOX	RNBCY	INHYW	HDDAL
NAPAG	ODHIR	AGNPA	DOGYR
ADOAO	HSRHD	TNHIH	CYNCH
NRHAP	ODAGM	BRNHY	WMKAJ
JANCY	IRYWO	XRTOA	WCROA
NBRRJ	YATAD	RHYWM	KHNBR
RJOAN	HKLRR	YWOXR	XRHDO
HVXRH	YWOXR	OXAGN	HYWYH
OGDHB	NXAVS	NOXHO	PBRNX
CNXRC	DOAOC	NHVAY	NGTTH
OACYW	REAGO	BKOAM	RLCNX
RWOAW	CROAN	BRRJO	ANBRR
JJRDV	XHYVR	OAWDR	HTHKO
XRDRN	OXRDG	MPADC	YOXHO
NBRRJ	APWRH	OXLXH	OWDRH
TNTHK	VATRL	XRYLR	XHIRN
XGPPB	RWAPP	OXCNT	ADOHB
VACBT	GNOIC	ERGNJ	HGNR

R 56; H 34; Y 23; W 16; P 12; M 8; K 6; S 2; U 0;
O 47; N 34; D 22; G 15; T 12; L 7; I 5; F 1; Z 0;
A 40; X 27; C 19; B 14; J 9; V 7; E 3; Q 0.

When we compare this with the table of average frequencies of letters in English, we see at once that *R* in the code stands for the letter *E*, and that *O* stands for the letter *T*. These two letters can be identified with certainty in any passage as long as this.

The next most frequent letter in the coded passage is *A*, and comparison with our average table of frequencies shows that it must stand either for the letter *O* or for *A* itself. We cannot settle this choice until we have identified some other letters.

However, we shall not be able to identify any other letters by a simple count of how often they occur by themselves, because the passage is so short that there is too much room for fluctuation. Therefore we must now go on to a more subtle count; we must look for the frequency with which letters occur together in pairs. Far the most frequent pair of letters in English is *TH*, and far the most frequent pair of letters in this passage is *OX*. We can therefore be certain that *X* in the code stands for the letter *H*. (This is confirmed by the fact that the second most frequent pair of letters in the coded passage is *XR*, and the second most frequent pair of letters in average English is in fact *HE*.) We have succeeded in identifying one complete word in the text: the word *THE*.

We now look for longer combinations of the letters that we have identified, and we notice such a combination in lines 1, 12, and 17: this is the combination *OXHO*. It stands for *TH-T*, and we conclude that this must be the complete word *THAT*. Therefore *H* in the code stands for the English letter *A*.

This identification does two things. First, it settles the issue, whether *A* in the code stands for *O* or for *A*—it stands for the English letter *O*. And second, it gives us the end of line 10, *OXR XRHDO*, in the form *THE HEA-T*; from which it follows that *D* in the code stands for the English letter *R*.

We can now tackle the beginning of the passage firmly. It starts:

TO-EO R-OTT O-ETH AT--T HE--E -T-O-

Three of the repeated letters here *N*, *Y* and *C*, are among the most frequent letters in the passage; they are in fact the only three of the nine most frequent letters that we have not identified yet. When we look back to the table of average frequencies, we see that they must stand, in some order, for the English letters *S*, *N* and *I*. A small amount of experimenting, and a modest amount of good sense, shows that the beginning of our passage reads:

TO-EO RNOTT O-ETH ATIST HE--E STION

We have now effectively broken the code: the passage begins, obviously:

TOBEO RNOTT OBETH ATIST HEQUE STION

What we have been wrestling with is the famous speech of Hamlet,

> To be, or not to be, that is the question:
> Whether 'tis nobler in the mind to suffer
> The slings and arrows of outrageous fortune,
> Or to take arms against a sea of troubles,
> And by opposing end them? To die, to sleep,
> No more; and by a sleep, to say we end
> The heartache and the thousand natural shocks
> That flesh is heir to, 'tis a consummation
> Devoutly to be wished. To die, to sleep—
> To sleep, perchance to dream; ay, there's the rub.
> For in that sleep of death, what dreams may come,
> When we have shuffled off this mortal coil,
> Must give us pause.

The numbers of the letters in this passage, now that we have it clear and not in code, are:
E 56; A 34; N 23; D 16; F 12; B 8; Y 6; K 2; X 0;
T 47; S 34; R 22; U 15; M 12; C 7; G 5; Q 1; Z 0;
O 40; H 27; I 19; L 14; P 9; W 7; V 3; J 0.

This count shows quite wide variations from the standard table of average frequencies, which we gave earlier. One reason lies in the special form of the speech, in the deliberate choice of short and harsh words which Shakespeare used to give the speech its troubled, halting tone. Yet this in itself is part of a more general and purely statistical reason, which is that the speech is a single extract from a larger and much more varied work. If we were to count all the letters in *Hamlet*, we should get numbers which come quite near to the average frequencies in the standard table.

In short, the smaller the sample of any statistical arrangement that we take, the more we must expect it to depart from the average. It is the nature of small samples to be exceptional—and the smaller, the more exceptional. We can illustrate this by taking only the first 100 letters of the same speech of Hamlet.

> To be, or not to be, that is the question:
> Whether 'tis nobler in the mind to suffer
> The slings and arrows of outrageous fortune.

These 100 letters are divided like this:
T 14; N 8; H 6; A 4; D 2; W 2; K 0; X 0;
E 12; R 8; I 6; F 4; G 2; M 1; C 0; P 0; Y 0;
O 12; S 8; U 5; B 3; L 2; Q 1; J 0; V 0; Z 0.
Here *E* is not even the commonest letter, and the distribution is quite irregular—for example, *U* is more frequent than *A*.

There is in all this a close analogy with the behaviour of physical events, as we described them in the last chapter—with the behaviour of atoms, of photons of light, and of grains of sand or pollen. The distribution of a large handful of pollen grains between the compartments in a box is predictable, just as the distribution of the letters in a large book is predictable. But there is no way of telling where ten or twenty pollen grains will go, just as there is no way of knowing in advance what proportion of the letters in a very short passage will be *E*'s and what proportion will be *T*'s.

This idea, the idea of statistics, is now very important in physics. During the last fifty years we have come to realise that most of the laws of physics are of the same type as the law which states that 13 per cent of the letters in a book in English will be *E*'s. That is to say, most laws in physics are really statistical. They are true only of large collections of things and of events on a large scale.

As we saw in the last chapter, the nature and the behaviour of physical events on the small scale is unexpected. We can argue from small events to large ones, but we cannot argue the other way about. If we try to apply the laws of large-scale physics to small-scale events, they will mislead us. In just the same way, we should be misled if we argued that, because 13 per cent of the letters in this book are *E*'s, therefore every word of eight letters in it contains an *E*. In fact, 'contains' contains no *E*.

The phrases 'large collections of things' and 'events on a large scale' are rather vague. Let us therefore make them concrete by giving some practical (and everyday) examples.

Picture for yourself two familiar things: a toy balloon, and water coming out of a tap. Take first the toy balloon. It is kept distended by the pressure of the air inside it. We naturally think of the air inside as if it were pressing outwards evenly in all directions—after all, that is why the balloon is round. But air consists of molecules, and molecules cannot press evenly on anything. They are in continual motion, bouncing backwards and forwards at great speeds. The pressure that the molecules exert is dynamic, not static; it pushes here and there, it constantly changes. Yet in large enough numbers, the changing effects of the molecules as they rush about add up to a steady force.

Again, in our daily experience water seems to flow steadily out of the tap. But water also consists of molecules, and they cannot flow in a steady stream. There are molecules moving in all directions —at any moment, some of them are even moving backwards, in the opposite direction to the general flow. The general flow is an average effect, which is shared by the majority of the molecules, but not by all. In fact, the constituent molecules of the water coming out of the tap (and of the air in the balloon) obey quite different laws from the laws which describe their combined effect. When we turn on the tap, we can be sure that water will flow out; but we cannot be sure what an individual molecule will do.

We will take a last example, not from physics, but from biology. In biology, the effect of statistical laws is slow but profound. Statistical laws lead to the decline of one species and the rise of another. This is how evolution comes about, and we will take a practical example of evolution as it has actually happened in England in quite recent times.

The first picture below shows two moths against the same background—a tree covered with lichen, as found in an open and clean countryside. One moth is light-coloured, and is almost invisible against the clean background; the other moth is dark, and is

clearly visible. Both moths are specimens of the British Peppered Moth; the light-coloured moth used to be the normal type, and the dark moth is a mutant which occurs from time to time, yet which was almost unknown a hundred years ago—it first began to be noticed about 1848. But since 1848, the dark moths have become more and more common, and the light-coloured moths of the same species have become rarer and rarer. The second picture shows why this has happened; it shows the two moths on a modern background—a tree blackened by the soot of industry. With the coming of industry, the light moth has become more conspicuous than the dark.

Birds catch the moths, and the dark ones were far more conspicuous against a light-coloured tree before the coming of industry. The dark moths were then more likely to be eaten; so that even though the mutation was occurring all the time, it was constantly eliminated. By 1848, however, the Industrial Revolution was well under way in England. One result was the blackening of trees and rocks in the industrial Midlands. On a black background, the light moths are more likely to be caught, as the second picture shows. In consequence, the dark variety of the Peppered Moth has now almost replaced the light variety in the industrial Midlands of England.

The dark moths did not suddenly take over. They gradually became more numerous when the probability of their getting caught became less. By careful experiments, Dr. H. B. D. Kettlewell (who took these pictures) has been able to put a numerical value on this probability. In an unpolluted area, a dark-coloured moth has a probability of survival which is nearly 20 per cent smaller than the prob-ability that a light-coloured moth will survive. Therefore in unpolluted areas the dark-coloured moths are still quite rare. But in a grimy, smoke-polluted area, it is the other way about. Here a dark-coloured moth has a probability of survival which is at least 10 per cent greater than the probability that a light-coloured moth will survive. So, gradually, the dark-coloured moths have become the common type in the industrial Midlands. Today, after only 100 years or so, they form 99 per cent of the population of Peppered Moths there.

A dark moth may survive in a non-industrial area, and a light moth may survive in smoke. There is no certainty about an individual moth. A single moth is like a single grain of pollen or a single letter in a book. No one can speak about it with certainty in advance. But we can say what is likely to happen to it, and if there are enough moths we can certainly predict the effect of a change in the environment.

Letters in the alphabet, molecules of water or air, the survival of moths—these things seem at first to have little in common. Yet they have in common the most important of all modern ideas in science: the idea of statistics. Their behaviour is governed by laws not of certainty but of probability. The individual behaviour is only probable, but the total behaviour of larger and larger collections becomes more and more nearly certain. What an individual letter will be, what one molecule will do, what will happen to a single moth—these are unpredictable. But take enough of any of these unpredictable events, and their total obeys laws which are precise and predictable.

9

THE STATISTICS OF HEALTH

In the last chapter, we looked at events which are individually unpredictable, yet whose total becomes predictable when we take large enough numbers of them. Medical statistics are also of this kind: they tell us about groups of people but not about individuals. Death rates and birth rates, for example, enable us to predict changes in population. They are useful to the social planner, but they are not useful in the same way to the doctor who is treating a patient. Knowing the death rate for a disease will not tell the doctor whether his patient is going to die of it. (Perhaps we ought to be pedantic and add, unless the disease is always fatal.) The death rate is essentially an average. By contrast, the doctor in treating his patient is concerned with the individual—with the single, unpredictable event.

Nevertheless, the statistics of life and death can help to guide the doctor. They can do this precisely by establishing the individuality of the patient—by showing how far his responses follow the average, and how far they depart from it. What the doctor does is to look for deviations from the average; and it is from the statistics, which are the collective experiences of others and of himself, that he knows what the average is.

Let us illustrate this procedure by a simple example. Everyone knows that the first step in any diagnosis is taking the temperature. Why? Because the temperature of the patient should be normal— that is, average. The doctor is looking for deviations from the average. If the patient's temperature deviates from the average, then something is wrong.

This is the way that statistics are used in diagnosis. We shall do best to follow it for a single disease. Here we will take the common heart-attack—that is, coronary thrombosis, which is an important cause of death in the well-to-do parts of the world today.

The two graphs on the next page show death rates in the United Kingdom from coronary thrombosis. The first graph gives the deaths per million inhabitants, year by year, for the last sixty years or so. Probably the figures for the early years are not very reliable; nevertheless, there is no doubt that more and more people are dying of coronary thrombosis every year.

There are also quite marked differences between the death rates for men and for women. (The higher line is for men, the lower line for women.) In the last twenty years, the death rate for men has increased nearly threefold. The death rate for women has increased only by about one half.

The second graph shows the death rates now, in the different age groups. Again we see the difference between the sexes. Coronary thrombosis is a disease of middle age, in men and in women. But men are now dying of it often before they reach forty, whereas there are few deaths among women before the age of forty-five years. At higher ages, women have more nearly the same death rate as men. And beyond the age of seventy or so, women die of coronary thrombosis even more often than men.

These are the barest statistics of the disease: the number of people of either sex who die of it, and at what ages. What the doctor wants is to find a logical thread in these statistics that will help him to guide people away from this form of death.

The words 'coronary thrombosis' mean a clot of blood in one of the arteries in the heart. A clot does not normally form without a cause, spontaneously. It is usually preceded by a furring up of the arteries with some fatty material such as cholesterol. The fur gradually narrows the arteries and encourages

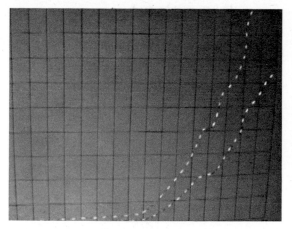

the formation of clots. The coronary thrombosis is caused by a clot, but it is the furring up of the arteries that produces the danger.

Medical specialists think that there are three main causes which make the arteries fur up. They are lack of exercise, stress, and too much to eat; and they are dramatically illustrated in the pictures at the bottom of the next two pages.

Lack of exercise seems a reasonable cause. Stress is more difficult to pin down. Roughly it means worry, tension, unhappiness. It is often found in people whose jobs carry much responsibility and who have to make many decisions. Not all specialists agree that stress is an important contributor to coronary thrombosis. Everyone is agreed, however, that overeating is a serious cause. The fat on meat and in dairy products may be particularly dangerous.

If this analysis is right, it helps to explain why coronary thrombosis kills fewer women than men, and kills them more slowly. Even in doing house-work, women get more exercise than many men; they are less exposed to stress; and they usually eat less. And there is also another, physical factor in-volved. Women of child-bearing age are protected to some extent by their hormones. These hormones

keep down the level of fat, particularly of cholester-ol, in the blood, and so the furring up of the arteries is delayed. This effect is quite definite—for example, it can be seen in autopsies.

Thus the statistics point to, and the other medical evidence confirms, the factors which prompt or pre-vent the onset of coronary thrombosis: age, sex, exercise, stress and diet. These are therefore the factors into which a doctor enquires when he fears that his patient is in danger of coronary thrombosis.

The consultation which follows, and which is given word for word, shows how a great specialist weighs the various factors as he makes up his mind about a case. The consultation was not rehearsed. The doctor who allowed us to witness it, as part of a programme of *Insight*, simply gave us his list of future appointments. We chose a new patient from the list without telling the doctor who he was. He was, in fact, a patient whose brother the doctor had already treated; we wanted to see whether the doctor (if he discovered this) gave any weight to such family links. For obvious reasons, the patient (below) will be called Mr. X; and the doctor (on the left) was of course anonymous in the programme.

Doctor: Mr. X, you've brought me, I see, one or two facts. I'm afraid I haven't got your age.
Patient: Thirty-nine.
Doctor: Thirty-nine—fairly young. Do you mind if I ask you some personal questions?
Patient: Please do, sir.
Doctor: First of all, your occupation?
Patient: A bank messenger.
Doctor: A bank messenger. I'm sorry, I should know what a bank messenger does, but I'm not too clear. What exactly do you do?
Patient: Well, I make my calls mainly, quite a lot of walking. You know, from bank to bank in the City.
Doctor: Any stress attached to your job?
Patient: Not for me personally, no.
Doctor: You don't handle the bullion?
Patient: No—no. Nothing like that.
Doctor: No chance of being knocked on the head, for example?
Patient: No.
Doctor: So really, your life is not full of stress?
Patient: Not really, no.
Doctor: May I ask just why you are seeking medical advice?
Patient: Yes, in 1955 my brother died of coronary thrombosis.
Doctor: I am sorry to hear that.
Patient: And there is another brother who is in hospital now, also with coronary thrombosis.
Doctor: I see.
Patient: And I wondered whether there was any connection between them and myself.
Doctor: Yes, of course that's sensible. Are there any more brothers?
Patient: One more, yes.
Doctor: Is he all right?
Patient: Apparently, yes.
Doctor: There were four of you altogether?
Patient: Yes.
Doctor: Have you any reason to think, apart from this bad family history, that you could have some fault with your coronary arteries?
Patient: No sir, no.
Doctor: You don't get any pain in the chest if you hurry?
Patient: No.
Doctor: And no pain in the legs?
Patient: No.
Doctor: You've never had a clot in a vein or any part of you?
Patient: Not to my knowledge, no.
Doctor: In fact you're a very normal, healthy sort of man?
Patient: Yes.
Doctor: I see. Well now I have to ask about your habits. First of all, exercise. You tell me you walk a lot in your job. Do you take exercise in addition to that?
Patient: Yes, I'm quite keen on cycling, and I've done a great deal in the past.
Doctor: Do you cycle long distances?
Patient: I have done, yes.
Doctor: What do you mean?
Patient: A hundred—a hundred and fifty miles in a day.
Doctor: Do you race?
Patient: I have done, yes.
Doctor: This is all splendid. If exercise protects you, you should be protected. Some people think that. And what about smoking?
Patient: No.
Doctor: You don't smoke?
Patient: No, and I never have done.
Doctor: Not at all?
Patient: No, not at all.
Doctor: Indeed. That's another good thing. Now what about the question of diet?
Patient: Oh, I'm a good eater.
Doctor: A good eater—
Patient: Yes.
Doctor: Fat too?
Patient: Yes, almost anything.
Doctor: Butter, milk, top of the milk, cream, eggs? All these things?
Patient: Yes.
Doctor: You don't cut the fat off roast meat?
Patient: No, I enjoy it.
Doctor: That I'm afraid does count against you, particularly with this bad family history. If it should concern the blood fat. Of course, we don't know that yet. Do you have the record of the tests that were made on you today? Oh, I see, here. The tests show your blood pressure is 115 over 75, this is absolutely excellent, and very much in your favour. But your cholesterol level, that's

one of the blood fats, is 450 milligrams per cent. This I'm afraid is a fairly high figure, Mr. X. In fact, it's about twice as high as it should be. Do you know whether one of your brothers has a high cholesterol too?

Patient: I don't know for certain, no.

Doctor: No, I see. It might be that it's running in the family. At this level there could be— you haven't any little spots? May I see your hands? Sometimes if the cholesterol is very high it comes out under the skin, perhaps in the tendons, sometimes in the eyelids. I wonder if you could just clench your fists, could

you? Yes, you see we have here two little yellow nodules—have you noticed them yourself, Mr. X?

Patient: I have, yes. I've had these for some time actually.

Doctor: Really? Well, I'm sorry to say that that really is cholesterol. This is really most interesting, most astonishing in fact. This high cholesterol is very important.

This was a dramatic moment in the programme. The doctor's questions had led him to a symptom which was very far from normal, and it was there for all to see, in the knuckles of the patient's hands. Evidently the fatty cholesterol in the patient's blood-

stream was being deposited at points in the body.

The high cholesterol level in this patient's blood dominates the case. The fact that he is a man, living in the 1960's and in well-to-do England, counts against him; however, there is nothing he can do about that. The exercise he takes is in his favour, and his job does not expose him to stress. But the amount of cholesterol in his blood is potentially dangerous. It has not made him ill, but it could do so in the future.

The doctor asked about levels of cholesterol in the patient's brothers because high cholesterol often runs in families. Two other factors that increase the likelihood of coronary thrombosis are also often inherited. One is high blood pressure, the other is a tendency to form blood clots. In this patient, both were fairly normal.

Where blood cholesterol and blood pressure are concerned, normal means average. There is no 'correct' figure for either. Both vary quite considerably, even in a population of healthy people. The variations are distributed round an average, and moderate deviations from the average cause no alarm. When a doctor says that a patient has a high blood pressure or high blood cholesterol, and shows alarm, he means more than that the blood pressure or the cholesterol is above average. He means that the deviation from the average is much more than moderate. That is what alarms him.

A doctor diagnoses on the basis of deviations from averages. A slight deviation from the average does not mean that anything is wrong. But a large deviation warns the doctor that something is going wrong. In particular, a large deviation from the average level of cholesterol in the blood is frequently associated with coronary thrombosis.

Sometimes a great specialist can give a numerical value to the risk attached to a large deviation from the average. For example, the doctor in this programme held that a man with high blood pressure is twice as likely to get coronary thrombosis as a man with normal blood pressure. And heavy smoking, he held, increases the danger one and a half times. So a man with high blood pressure who is also a heavy smoker would be three times as likely to get coronary thrombosis as would a man with neither abnormality.

It is on statistics of this kind that the doctor bases his treatment. In the case of Mr. X, for example, the long term aim would be to reduce the level of cholesterol in the blood. That would take time; meanwhile he would be protected with drugs which stop the blood from clotting. If Mr. X's blood pressure had been high, the treatment would have been directed to reduce that.

Coronary thrombosis is still imperfectly under-stood. We cannot say what causes it with the same certainty that we can say that a particular infection causes typhoid. That is why the statistics of the disease are important. They show what kind of people have it, at what age, and that it is associated with high blood pressure and high cholesterol. In this way, the statistical observations suggest the possible lines of treatment.

It does not follow of itself that treatments to lower the blood pressure or to reduce the cholesterol will in fact prevent a coronary thrombosis. The statistics show that there is an association between them and the disease, but they do not in themselves show that either abnormality causes the disease. It could be that some factor that we have not yet observed causes the cholesterol to form in the patient's blood and at the same time gives him coronary thrombosis.

We cannot always jump to the conclusion that an association establishes a cause. Statistics can show that in English, the letter T is often followed by the letter H; but this does not prove that the letter T causes the letter H to appear! Statistics are valuable in showing an association, and the association suggests that a link of cause and effect exists; but it then remains to trace the exact chain of causes to effect. For example, statistics show that there is an association between bad housing and rickets; yet this does not mean that bad housing causes rickets— or even that poverty causes rickets directly. There is a causal chain, but it has to be traced more precisely and with more care than this.

Reasoning from statistics needs care—and honesty. We can see the need for both in the current debates about lung cancer. Does heavy cigarette smoking cause lung cancer? Statistics show that there is a definite association between them. But as many people point out (particularly heavy smokers), an association does not prove a cause. In themselves, the statistics might be explained in other ways. Perhaps people who are getting lung cancer develop a craving to smoke cigarettes, and we ought not to frighten them off this small comfort? Perhaps the desire to smoke and a tendency to lung cancer are both inherited, or are both caused by the weather, or by the stress of modern life? Perhaps smoking causes people to drink, and alcohol is the real cause of lung cancer?

None of these suggestions is impossible, even though few of them are honest. All have to be studied, and they have been—and have been shown not to hold water. The fact is that the association between heavy cigarette smoking and lung cancer rests on much more detailed evidence than crude overall statistics, and this total evidence leaves no doubt now that smoking is directly responsible. If you smoke many cigarettes, your risk of getting lung cancer goes up. If you stop smoking, the risk goes down again.

Yet because lung cancer is only a risk, a probability, many people find it hard to be convinced (at least, to give up smoking). Statistics do not seem to have the finality of more direct evidence, and people find it harder to be guided by them. It would be different, they feel, if all heavy smokers got lung cancer; then they would be persuaded. But while the evidence is only statistical, they prefer to doubt it— or at least to forget it.

Reasoning from statistics is a new skill, young and unfamiliar. In time, no doubt, it will become common, and people will weigh probabilities as naturally as they now tell black from white. But the time is still some way off, until new generations learn this way of thinking.

There is a sad postscript to this chapter. It can now be revealed that the doctor whose consultation we witnessed was Paul Hamilton Wood, the Director of the Institute of Cardiology. He was the outstanding specialist in the diagnosis of heart disease, and a pioneer in its study and treatment. The patient, Mr. X has progressed well under his treatment. Dr. Wood died of a heart attack at the age of fifty-five on 14th July, 1962.

PART FOUR—THE NATURE OF TIME

10

THE ARROW OF TIME

This chapter and those that follow deal with time. In particular, this chapter looks at the direction of time. Why does time go one way only? Why cannot we turn time backwards? Why are we not able to travel in time, back and forth?

The idea of time travel has fascinated men. Even folklore contains legends about travel in time. And science fiction, from *The Time Machine* onwards, has been pre-occupied with this theme. Plainly, men feel themselves to be imprisoned in the single direction of time. They would like to move about in time as freely as they can move in space.

And time is in some way like space. Like space, time is not a thing but is a relation between things. The essence of space is that it describes an order

among things—higher or lower, in front or behind, to left or to right. The essence of time also is that it describes an order—earlier or later. Yet we cannot move things in time as we can in space. Time must therefore describe some fundamental process in nature which we do not control.

It is not easy to discuss time without bringing in some way of measuring it—a clock of one sort or another. Yet if all the clocks in the world stopped, and if we all lost all inner sense of time, we could still tell earlier from later. The essential nature of time does not depend on clocks. That is the point of this chapter, and we will begin by illustrating it

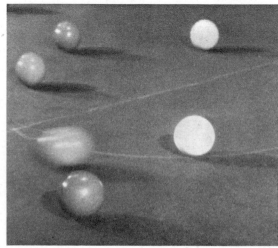

from very simple and common experiences.

The three pairs of pictures point the way. They help to show what it is that enables us to tell earlier from later without a clock. In each pair, the pictures are arranged at random, and not necessarily in the sequence of time. Yet in all except the first pair, it is easy to arrange the pictures; the sequence in time is obvious. Only the first pair does not betray its time sequence. What is the difference between the first pair of pictures and the other two pairs?

We get a clue to the difference when we study the arrangement of the things in each picture. In the first pair, we cannot really distinguish one arrangement from another; they are equally tidy and orderly. The two pictures of the first pair show a shot at billiards. The billiard balls are as well arranged after the shot as before; there is no obvious difference between the arrangements.

The situation is different in the other two pairs. A broken egg is an entirely different arrangement from a whole egg. A snooker pyramid is quite different from a jumble of balls.

And not only are the arrangements here different. Once they are different, it is quite clear which arrangement comes before the other. Whole eggs come before broken ones. The snooker pyramid comes before the spread of the balls.

In each case, the earlier arrangement is more ordered than the later. Time produces disorder; that is the lesson of these pictures. And it is also the lesson of this chapter. The arrow of time is loss of order.

In a game of snooker, we know quite well that the highly ordered arrangement of the balls at the beginning of the game comes before the disordered arrangement at the end of the first shot. Indeed, the first shot is called 'breaking the pyramid'; and breaking is a destructive action—it destroys order. It is just not conceivable that fifteen balls would gather themselves up into a pyramid, however skilful the player. The universe does not suddenly create order out of disorder.

These pictures show the same thing again. When a spot of powdered dye is put on the surface of water, it spreads out and gradually dissolves. Dye would never come out of solution and stream together by itself to gather in a spot on the surface. Again time is breaking down order and making disorder. It disperses the dye randomly through the water.

We know at once that the stones in the picture below were shaped and erected a very long time ago. Their rough, weathered surfaces bear the mark of time. It is still possible to reconstruct the once orderly arrangement of the stones of Stonehenge. But the once orderly surface of each stone cannot be recovered. Atom by atom, the smooth surface has been carried away, and is lost to chaos.

And here finally is the most interesting of all the pictures in which time betrays itself. In these shots from an old film the heroine has been tied to the rails—a splendid tradition of silent films. A train is approaching, but of course it stops just in time. The role of the heroine would seem to call for strong nerves as well as dramatic ability, if she has to trust the engine driver to stop the locomotive exactly where he is told. However, the last few yards of the approach are in fact done by a trick. The locomotive is *started* close to the heroine and is backed away; and the film is then run backwards.

There is only one thing that gives this trick away. When the film is run backwards, the smoke visibly goes into the funnel instead of coming out of it. We know that in reality, smoke behaves like the spreading dye: it becomes more disorderly, the further it gets from the funnel. So when we see disorder coming before order, we realise that something is wrong. Smoke does not of itself collect together and stream down a funnel.

One thing remains to clear up in these examples. We began with an example in which earlier and later were equally well ordered. The example was a shot at billiards. The planets in their orbits would be another example, in which there would be nothing to say which arrangement comes first.

Then does time stand still in billiards and planetary motion? No, time is still doing its work of disorder. We may not see the effects at once, but they are there. For billiard balls and planets gradually lose material from their surface, just like the stones of Stonehenge. Time destroys their orderly shape too. A billiard ball is not quite the same after a shot

as before it. A planet is not quite the same in each successive orbit. And the changes are in the direction of disorder. Atoms are lost from ordered structures and return to chaos. The direction of time is from order to disorder.

That is one reason why perpetual motion machines are impossible. Time cannot be brought to a standstill. We cannot freeze the arrangement of the atoms, even in a tiny corner of the universe. And that is what we should have to do to make a perpetual motion machine. The machine would have to remain the same, atom for atom, for all time. Time would have to stand still for it.

For example, take the first of these three machines from a famous book of Perpetual Motion Machines. It is meant to be kept going by balls in each sector, which roll from the centre to the rim and back again as the wheel turns. Of course it does not work. There is friction in the bearing of the wheel, and more friction between the balls and the tracks they run on. Every movement rubs off a few atoms. The bearings wear, the balls lose their smooth roundness. Time does not stand still.

The second machine is more complicated and sillier. It is designed to work like a waterwheel with little balls instead of water. At the bottom the balls roll out of their compartments down the chute, and on to a moving belt which is to lift them to the top again. That is how the machine is meant to keep going. In fact, when we built it, it came to a stop every few minutes.

The pendulum arrangement in the third picture also comes from the book of Perpetual Motion Machines. A ball runs backwards and forwards in the trough on top to keep it going. There are also elastic strings at each end for good measure. This machine at least works for short bursts. But as a perpetual motion machine, it has the same defects as the others. Nothing can be done to get rid of friction; and where there is friction, there must be wear.

This last point is usually put a little differently. Every machine has friction. It has to be supplied with energy to overcome the friction. And this energy cannot be recovered. In fact, this energy is lost in heat, and in wear—that is, in moving atoms out of their order, and in losing them. That is another way of putting the same reasoning, and shows equally (in different language) why a perpetual motion machine cannot work.

Before we put these fanciful monsters out of mind, it is worth seeing how beautifully a fine machine can be made. It cannot conquer the disorder of time, it cannot get rid of friction, but it can keep them to a minimum. So here on this page are two splendid clocks which make no pretence to do the impossible, yet which go as far as it is possible to go by means of exact and intelligent craftsmanship.

These clocks are not intended to be perpetual motion machines. Each has an outside source of energy to keep it going. In the clock at the top, it is ordinary clockwork which tips the platform whenever the ball has completed a run. The clock below is more tricky: it has no clockwork spring, and instead is driven by temperature differences in the air. But even if there was someone to wind one clock, and suitable air conditions for the other, they could not run for ever. They would wear out. That is, their ordered structure would slowly become more disordered until they stopped. The clock with no spring would run for several hundred years, but it could not run for ever.

To summarise: the direction of time in the universe is marked by increasing disorder. Even without clocks and without an inner sense of time, we could tell later and earlier. 'Later' is characterised by the greater disorder, by the growing randomness of the universe.

We ought to be clear what these descriptive phrases mean. Order is a very special arrangement; and disorder means the loss of what makes it special. When we say that the universe is becoming more disordered, more random, we mean that the special arrangements in this place or that are being evened out. The peaks are made lower, the holes are filled in. The extremes disappear, and all parts sink more and more towards a level average. Disorder and randomness are not wild states; they are simply states which have no special arrangement, and in which everything is therefore near the average.

Even in disorder, of course, things move and deviate round their average. But they deviate by chance, and chance then takes them back to the average. It is only in exceptional cases that a deviation becomes fixed, and perpetuates itself. These exceptions are fascinating and important, and we now turn to them.

The movement towards randomness, we repeat, is not uniform. It is statistical, a general trend. And (as we saw in Chapter 8) the units that make up a general trend do not all flow in the same direction. Here and there, in the midst of the flow towards an average of chaos, there are places where the flow is reversed for a time. The most remarkable of these reversals is life. Life as it were is running against time. Life is the very opposite of randomness.

How this can come about can be shown by an analogy. The flow of time is like an endless shuffling of a pack of cards. A typical hand dealt after long

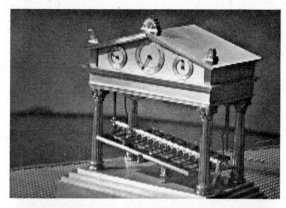

shuffling will be random—say four diamonds, a couple of spades, four clubs, and three hearts. This is the sort of hand a bridge player expects to pick up several times in an evening. Yet every now and then a bridge player picks up a freak hand. For example, from time to time a player picks up all thirteen spades. And this does not mean that the pack was not properly shuffled. A hand of thirteen spades can arise by chance, and does; the odds against it are high, but they are not astronomic. Life started with a chance accident of this kind. The odds against it were high, but they were not astronomic.

The special thing about life is that it is self-perpetuating. The freak hand, instead of disappearing in the next shuffle, reproduces itself. Once the thirteen spades of life are dealt, they keep their order, and they impose it on the pack from then on. This is what distinguishes life from other freaks, other deviations from the average.

There are other happenings in the universe that run against the flow of time for a while. The formation of a star from the interstellar dust is such a happening. When a star is formed, the dust that forms it becomes less random; its order is increased, not decreased. But stars do not reproduce themselves. Once the star is formed, the accident is over. The flow towards disorder starts again. The deviation begins to ebb back towards the average.

Life is a deviation of a special kind; it is a self-reproducing accident. Once its highly ordered arrangement occurs, once the thirteen spades happen to be dealt in one hand, it repeats itself. The order was reached by chance, but it then survives because it is able to perpetuate itself, and to impose itself on other matter.

It is rare to find in *dead* matter behaviour of this kind which illustrates the way in which *life* imposes its order. An analogy of a kind, however, is found in the growth of crystals. When a supercooled solution is ready to form crystals, it needs something to start it off. Now we introduce the outside accident, the freak hand at bridge. That is, we introduce a tiny crystal that we have made, and we drop it in. At once the crystal starts to grow and to impose its own shape round it.

In this analogy, the first crystal is a seed, like the seed of life. Without it, the supercooled solution would remain dead, unchanged for hours or even days. And like the seed of life, the first crystal imposes its order all round it. It reproduces itself many times over.

Nearly five hundred years ago, Leonardo da Vinci described time as the destroyer of all things. So we have seen it in this chapter. It is the nature of time to destroy things, to turn order into disorder. This indeed gives time its single direction—its arrow.

But the arrow of time is only statistical. The general trend is towards an average chaos; yet there are deviations which move in the opposite direction. Life is the most important deviation of this kind. It is able to reproduce itself, and so to *perpetuate the order which began by accident*. Life runs against the disorder of time.

11

TIME IN LIFE AND DEATH

In the last chapter we looked at the nature of time. Time is an arrow with one direction: when it points from earlier to later, it points in the direction of growing disorder.

By contrast, life runs against the flow of time. Life continually makes order out of chaos, and builds new arrangements and structures in the midst of the drift towards disorder.

These pictures vividly show life at its task of building. They are pictures of tiny single-celled amoebae, the slime moulds, which form the slimy growth often found on decaying wood. These moulds are also called the social amoebae, for reasons that the pictures make evident. Most of the time, the slime

moulds lead individual existences, as normal amoebae do. But every now and then they move together, perhaps in response to some chemical signal released

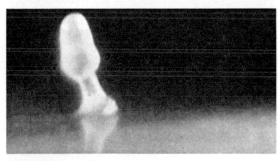

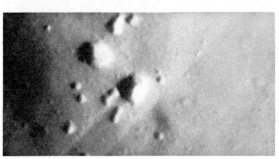

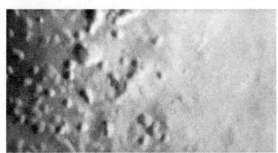

by one of them; and then they form themselves into a single, compact, slug-like body of thousands of cells. This body lengthens, changes its shape, and, in time, bursts and scatters its spores. These spores grow into single amoebae and the cycle starts all over again.

The social amoebae are a striking and picturesque example of the complex orders which the processes of life build and maintain. In this chapter, we shall look at three kinds of such processes. First, we shall see how living things choose from their environment the chemicals that they need, and how they modify them for their use. Second, we shall see how living things resist decay, actively, in order to preserve their order. And third, we shall see how living things can re-create quite complex parts of themselves which have been damaged or wholly lost.

First, then, how living things choose the chemicals that they need, and modify them for their use. We shall take our example from the mechanism of vision. The picture above on the left is a model of the molecule of vitamin A. The picture on the right above shows part of the molecule of visual purple, which is the essential chemical that enables the eye to see. Vitamin A and visual purple are closely related; the change from one to the other, and back again, is fundamental to the process of seeing. Vitamin A is a necessary part of the human diet, which we get from our environment; and we then turn it into visual purple in order to see with it.

Below is part of the model of the eye we used in Chapter 7. This picture from the model shows

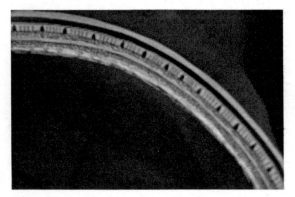

part of the retina, with the rods and cones on it. There are, we recall, about a hundred million rods and about six million cones in the eye—well over a hundred million receptors. When either type of receptor is struck by a photon of light, it undergoes a chemical change, and this change sends an electrical impulse along the optic nerve to the brain.

Visual purple and vitamin A are the two ends of this chemical change. Each rod and each cone contains visual purple, and it is this that changes. When a photon strikes a molecule of visual purple, it turns it into vitamin A.

The models of the two molecules at the top of the page show us what happens in detail. The picture on the right shows the molecule of visual purple in its normal state, as it is found in receptors that have not been exposed to light. It is mainly carbon and hydrogen, with a single atom of oxygen at the top end. The most distinctive thing about the molecule is its shape—compare it with the shape of the vitamin A molecule on the left. The two molecules are the same in all respects except one: in visual purple, the straight chain of vitamin A has a twist. The effect of a photon, when it strikes a molecule of visual purple, is to straighten out this twist; this turns it back into vitamin A.

The change can actually be seen, though not, of course, on the molecular scale. Visual purple has a colour; as its name implies, it is purple. Vitamin A is colourless. When light strikes the visual purple, it bleaches it. This is the visible effect of the straightening of the molecule, and it can be seen in the picture at the top of the next page. Both test-tubes contain visual purple: one has not been exposed to the light, the other has.

If the chemical remained bleached as vitamin A, the receptors would no longer be able to respond to light. But as soon as it has been bleached, the body turns it back into visual purple. Thus the cycle can start all over again.

Which of the two molecules has more order: the visual purple, or the vitamin A? Both are highly ordered—after all, vitamin A is itself only made by living things. Can we say that the human body gives an extra order to the vitamin A which it takes from plants, when it turns it into visual purple? We can,

if we understand exactly what we mean, as follows.

Order is a very special arrangement. The more normal and average an arrangement is, the lower its order. The more special and exceptional it is, the higher its order. The molecule of vitamin A is a straight chain, and that is a straightforward, average arrangement. In the molecule of visual purple, the same chain has a twist. The twist takes the molecule away from the average; it makes the arrangement more special and exceptional.

When a photon of light strikes a molecule of visual purple, it takes out the twist; it lets the chain fall back to the average and neutral state. If the molecule is to be made active again, the body must lift it to the exceptional state; it must give it a twist, it must—as it were—wind it up. This is characteristic of the activity of life: it puts things into an exceptional, wound-up state, which the process of nature runs down again to the average.

These reflections lead us naturally to our second theme: how living things resist decay, actively. For the exceptional order of life is constantly threatened by decay, and, in the extreme, by death. And once death sets in, nature's general movement towards disorder takes over quickly. The special structures and complicated chemicals of life fall to pieces, and the rotting remains become part of the movement to disorder.

The forces of decay are at work all the time, and living things must be able to resist them in order to survive. One of the means by which life resists decay and maintains its order is our second example.

A hazard to all forms of life except the lowest is infection by bacteria. The human body has several means to fight infection. Here we shall be concerned with only one means, which in many ways is the most interesting. This is the capture of bacteria by some white blood corpuscles.

The body makes white blood corpuscles all the time, mainly in the bone marrow. Each corpuscle has a life of only two or three days; so if for some reason the body suddenly stops making them, there are none left after a few days. This is one of the saddest effects which I myself saw in the people who had been exposed to radiation from the atomic bombs in Hiroshima and Nagasaki. For one of the effects of radiation is to destroy the bone marrow in which white blood corpuscles are made. After a heavy dose of radiation, therefore, the body is unable to fight against bacteria. Many people in Hiroshima and Nagasaki died in the end because they could not fight off quite minor infections, such as sore throats and slightly septic cuts.

These pictures show how some white corpuscles in a healthy body fight against bacteria. A string of bacteria is being swallowed by white blood corpuscles. The corpuscles are the large, irregular shapes. The bacteria are the small string in the first picture like a string of beads. We see in these pictures three stages in the destruction of the bacteria by the white corpuscles, which engulf them step by step. Life is resisting the threat of decay at the first sign of invasion.

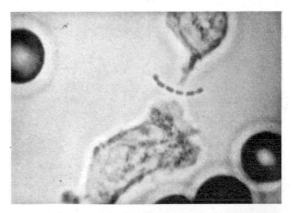

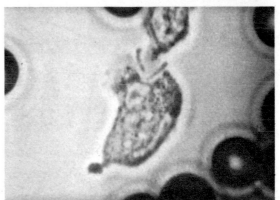

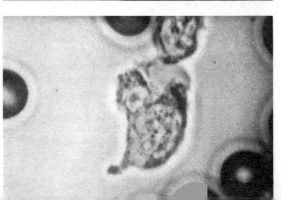

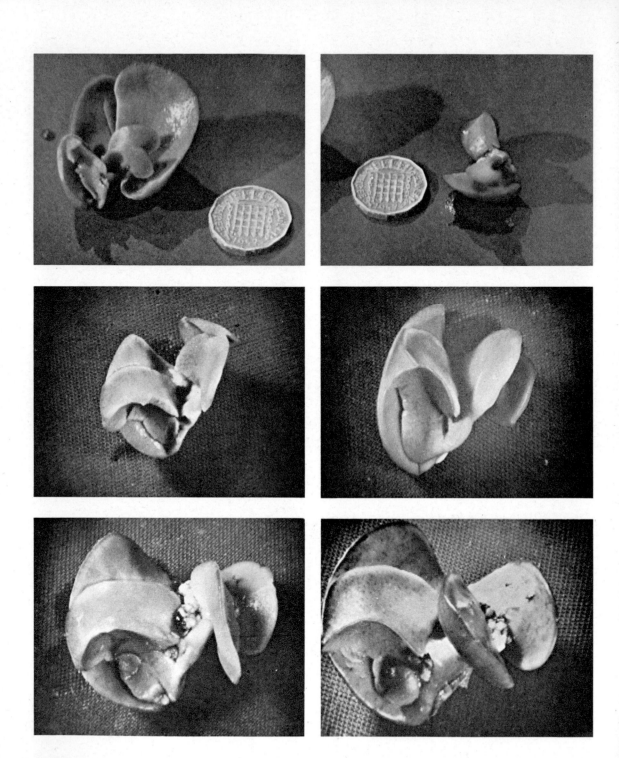

We turn now to our third theme: how living things can repair parts of themselves which have been damaged. Living things alone can do this; some can even remake lost parts. In general, dead matter can do nothing like this. A hole in a piece of metal will never repair itself, a broken brick will not join together again of itself. Yet all forms of life can repair and replace damaged tissues, and some animals can even replace lost limbs.

In human beings, the organ with the most remarkable power of regeneration is the liver. It is the largest of the inner organs, and it plays an important part in the body's chemistry. Food goes by way of the gut into the bloodstream, and the blood then carries it to the liver in order there to build up many of the chemicals that the body needs. That is, the liver is a chemical factory, which makes chemicals from the raw materials that reach it through the bloodstream. For example, muscles get their energy by burning sugar, and they get the sugar by way of the liver, which stores extra sugar and releases it as it is needed.

The liver is therefore extremely important, and the body is quick to repair it. The pictures on the left show the remarkable regeneration of the liver, even when it is greatly damaged. They are pictures of the liver of rats, but human liver recovers just as vigorously.

The first picture shows the complete liver of a rat. There is a threepenny piece beside it, to give an idea of the size.

The second picture shows a rat's liver extensively damaged; two-thirds of it has been lost.

Thereafter, the pictures show the extraordinary rate at which a rat's liver recovers, even after it has been damaged as much as this. Thus, the third picture is of the liver taken from a rat six hours after it had been damaged as much as this. The fourth picture shows how much the liver has recovered, twenty-four hours after the same damage. The fifth is after three days; by now, the damaged liver has doubled its size, so that it has recovered to two-thirds of its normal size. In the sixth picture, after five days, the liver is almost back to normal. The regeneration would be quite complete in ten days. (A human liver would regenerate in the same way, but not quite so fast.)

One striking thing about this regeneration is that it is so well controlled. Cells are dividing all the time, of course, even in a normal liver, in order to replace the ones that are worn out. Yet as soon as there is damage to be repaired, the liver cells at once start to multiply faster—almost a thousand times as fast as normal. We do not know what sets off the rapid growth, or what stops it when the liver gets back to its normal size. While the liver is regenerating, the cells are multiplying as fast as in a cancer; yet, unlike a cancer, the growth is perfectly controlled and orderly.

The growth of the damaged liver is remarkable. Yet more remarkable, more complicated by far is the regeneration of a complete limb. For the cells in the liver are largely of one kind; but a limb is made of skin, muscle, bone, nerves, blood vessels, and many other tissues, all of which have to be replaced from the beginning in the correct relations to one another. Of course, not all animals can grow new limbs. Mammals cannot, and birds cannot; but amphibians can.

The picture at the top of the page shows an

amphibian, the axolotl. These animals originally came from Mexico; now they are found in laboratories all over the world, partly because they are interesting, and partly because they do well in experiments. Axolotls are related to salamanders and newts. They have heads with two eyes, gills for breathing under water, bodies, tails which they use in swimming, and four legs. The pencil in the picture gives an idea of the animal's size.

Like most amphibians, axolotls catch their food by sight, and they will snap at anything that moves close to their heads. Inevitably, when a lot of axolotls are kept together, they snap at each other and occasionally bite off a leg. But when this happens, the damage is not permanent, as it is when a human being loses a leg. In the course of a few months, an axolotl will grow a perfectly good new leg to replace the lost one.

The picture below is an X-ray photograph of the bones in an axolotl's leg. They are very similar to those in a human arm, and not much less complicated. The other tissues do not show up in the X-ray, but they also are not much less complex than in the human arm.

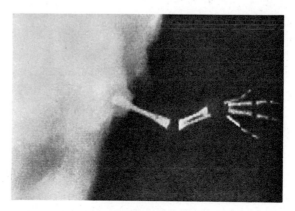

The next picture at the top of the next page is an X-ray photograph of an axolotl which has had part of a leg bitten off. The bone above the right elbow is intact; everything below the elbow is missing.

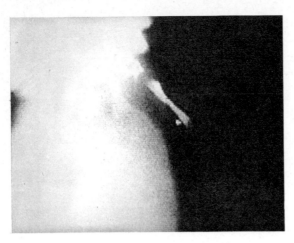

Now the gradual regeneration of the lost limb begins. The first picture in the next column was taken a few weeks after the accident. At the cut surface, there is an accumulation of new cells which show clearly against the background. These cells are the first material of the new limb. The next pictures show the animal with its complete new leg. Externally, it appears to be quite normal, and the X-ray photograph shows that this is indeed so. All the bony elements are present, and only a little more growth is needed to make the new limb exactly like the old.

The regeneration of a lost leg in the axolotl is fascinating to watch. It is also interesting as a biological problem. Where do the cells that make the new leg come from? How are they organised and controlled so that they make the right tissues in the right place? These questions can be answered, but there are still many questions that have not been answered.

In particular, why is it that some lower animals can regenerate whole limbs, while other and higher animals cannot? We ourselves, for example, can repair cuts in the skin and broken bones. We can even regenerate some lost tissues, such as the liver and the nerves. Yet we cannot regenerate a lost finger? Why not?

Research on animals like the axolotl should help to answer this question. For we now have reason to believe that there is a good deal in common between the healing of wounds in the higher animals and the regeneration of limbs in the lower. For example, we now know that young axolotls regenerate lost limbs more quickly than do old ones. Much the same is true of humans; wounds and broken bones mend faster in young people than in old. The study of regeneration in lower animals will give us greater insight into all the processes of healing. And greater insight will give us the possibility to extend and control our own healing.

Control over its own processes and control of its environment is an outstanding characteristic of life. In the last two chapters, we have seen how the environment constantly moves towards disorder, loss of pattern, to randomness and the monotony of the average. This is the direction of time. But life has the opposite direction. While time runs down, life seeks to build up—and to build more and more complex beings. Life is improbable, orderly, exceptional; it is a freak arrangement with the ability to reproduce itself. In a sense, life is a constantly repeated act of choice and of control, which imposes its pattern on nature again and again.

This chapter has illustrated three ways in which living things oppose and control the drift of nature towards disorder. First, they impose their own order on the food that they take from their environment. This is what the human body does when it twists the molecule of vitamin A in order to turn it into visual purple for the eye. Second, they resist even the threat of decay. This is what the body does when it makes white blood corpuscles which can swallow the bacteria that invade it. And third, living things can repair parts of themselves which have been damaged. This is what the human body does when it heals a cut; and in time, our researches may help to regenerate a lost leg.

12

THE RELATIVITY OF TIME

Few people will have any difficulty in recognising the man in this photograph, or in naming his greatest discovery. He is of course Albert Einstein, and he put forward the theory of relativity over fifty years ago. Einstein is perhaps the most famous scientist who has ever lived, and his theory the most famous scientific discovery.

Alas, the fame of the theory of relativity does not reach much beyond its name. Only a fraction of those who had heard of it understand it. Indeed, the theory of relativity has the reputation of being incomprehensible to all except a few brilliant physicists. This is quite untrue.

It is true that parts of the theory of relativity depend on difficult mathematics. But the main idea of relativity requires no mathematics. It requires only logic, and the ability to look at things in a way that is free from traditional habits. For though the theory of relativity first appeared over fifty years ago, in 1905, some of its implications are still fairly startling.

Relativity is not a formula. It is an idea, and a fundamental idea—one of the most important of the century. The idea concerns time, and it says this. We cannot change the direction of time. Time flows in the same *direction* for all of us. But it does not follow that time flows at the same *pace* for all of us. We must not assume that time passes at the same pace for a man who is moving as for a man who is standing still.

Einstein had asked himself questions about time when he was still a boy, long before he formed the theory of relativity. He began with a paradox that puzzled him at the age of sixteen. How would time pass for us if we were rushing through the universe at the greatest speed we know—the speed of light? If, for example, we watched a clock behind us, it would always show the same time, because the light coming from it would just keep pace with us. Then would time stand still for us in an everlasting, frozen moment?

The speed of light is closely bound up with the theory of relativity. The speed is very great; yet if we are to test the theory practically, we must be able to measure such speeds accurately. Fifty years ago, this needed a formidable array of machinery. Today it can be done with ease. It is worth while digressing

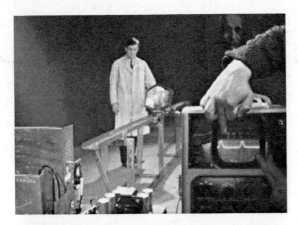

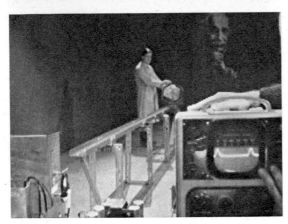

take ten seconds to get back, the mirror would have to be nearly a million miles away. Obviously, for the distances that we can use on earth, the intervals of time that we have to measure are very short indeed. The history of man's attempts to measure the speed of light is a record of more and more refined ways of measuring very short intervals of time.

Electronic devices now make it possible to time a light signal over a path which is only a few feet long. In the apparatus in the first picture, the mirror is only 15 feet away from the source of light and the timer. The picture also shows the trace on the timing screen of the time taken on the double journey, out and back, during which the light travels a total distance of 30 feet. The first peak on this screen marks the instant when the light was sent, and the second peak marks the instant when the light returns. The gap between the peaks gives the time that the light takes to get to the mirror and back again: just over thirty thousand-millionths of a second. The timing device itself is shown in more detail in the second picture. It is not a large piece of apparatus, yet it can measure thousand-millionths of a second. The third picture shows the trace when the mirror is 25 feet away and the light travels 50 feet altogether. The reading is now a little over fifty thousand-millionths of a second. So the speed of light is very close to one foot every thousand-millionth of a second.

Why is the speed of light important? Because it is the greatest speed at which we can exchange any information. This was the thought that led Einstein to his theory; that there is a limit to the speed with which we can pass information in the world, or indeed in the universe. The maximum speed is the speed of light, which is also the speed of radio waves. There is no way of sending a message, no way of exchanging information, faster than by light or by radio. People separated by 50 miles cannot communicate in less time than it takes light to travel 50 miles. If they are 500 miles apart, it must take them ten times longer. There is no short cut, and no way round this limit.

For example, think of a radio wave spreading out from London in all directions. The wave spreads in all directions and spreads very fast; yet it spreads at a perfectly finite speed. After three thousandths of a second the wave has just reached Marseille. There is no way in which the information carried by the wave could have got to Marseille in less than three thousandths of a second.

Perhaps the most dramatic way of putting this is to imagine that the sun is suddenly snatched from the sky. Light takes about eight minutes to reach us from the sun. So it would be eight minutes before it got dark on earth. And it could also be eight minutes

for a moment to look at a modern method for measuring these great speeds.

The principle of the method can be understood by a simple analogy with sound. One can get at least a rough idea of the speed of sound simply by timing an echo from a cliff which is a known distance away. The same principle will do to measure the speed of light, if we put a mirror in place of the cliff. The only difficulty is that light travels so fast. If we make a sound, the echo from a cliff a mile away gets back to us in about ten seconds. But for a light signal to before the sun's gravitational attraction failed and the earth flew out of its orbit. There is no way at all in which we could know in less than eight minutes that the sun was no longer in the sky. No two places in the universe can be linked faster than at the speed of light.

Einstein's great insight was to follow the implications of this thought to their end. One implication is that there is no single and absolute standard of time in the universe. There is no cosmic clock ticking away the seconds to which anybody can refer anywhere in the universe. Two people in two places can look at their watches and compare them; but between them there is still the gulf of space that cannot be spanned faster than a foot every thousand-millionth of a second. Time is relative, and it cannot be separated from space.

There is no universal 'now'; each of us has his own 'here and now'. When we travel we carry our time with us, and time only passes as fast as experience. If we could indeed travel at the speed of light, a foot every thousand-millionth of a second, time would not pass at all. We should have no experiences, the universe would appear frozen, and time would stand still for us. And the closer we come to the speed of light, the slower time passes for us.

An imaginary journey in space can show what this means in concrete terms. In the first picture at the top of this page, the earth is shown in front of a map of the stars. North is to the right and south to the left, both for the globe and the star map. The constellation of Hercules is in the top right-hand corner, and the constellation of Scorpio is halfway up the left-hand side. Between them is a star called Barnard's star, which is about six light-years distant from the earth. That is, the light from Barnard's star takes about six years to reach us.

The following pictures show an imaginary journey to Barnard's star and back to earth again. It is literally a round trip. We have chosen a circular path so that we need make no allowance for the time that it would otherwise take to stop and to turn round at Barnard's star.

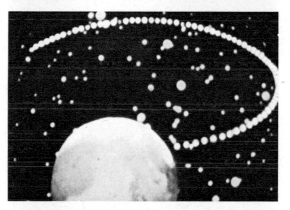

The circle is six light years across, so the circular path is (very roughly) 20 light-years long. According to those left behind on earth, a rocket travelling at the speed of light would therefore take 20 years to make the journey. Yet to a man inside the rocket (if he could travel so fast), time would stand still. Clocks would not have time to move, his heart would not have time to beat, and he would not age at all.

It is impossible for a rocket or any other thing to move at the speed of light. Instead, suppose the rocket travels at one-third of the speed of light. The

F

What do these differences in time mean? They do not mean that anything has travelled backwards in time. They mean that all processes in the speeding rocket have been slowed down. And this slowing down is not just a fancy in the mind. There is a real, physical slowing down. The clock in the speeding rocket has not ticked as many times as the clock which remained still on earth. Therefore the clock in the rocket has had less wear; it has truly aged less.

Biological processes are slowed down in the speeding rocket in exactly the same way as physical ones. The pulse of the man in the rocket does not beat as many times on the journey as the pulse of a man who remains behind on earth. So the man in the rocket truly ages less. He has had fewer heartbeats and fewer experiences. He is less worn, he looks younger than the man he left behind.

Some people have doubted this. How can we tell, they have said, that the man on the rocket has really been moving? Perhaps he kept still, and Barnard's star and the earth swung round to meet him? How do we know who made the round trip and who stayed at home?

These doubts are mistaken. The man on the round trip can tell that he is moving, exactly because he is going *round*. He feels the turning movement in his rocket, just as we feel it in a car going round a corner. Straight and steady movements cannot be

first two pictures here show the different rates at which time passes on earth and in the rocket. One clock registers the passage of time on earth, the other the passage of time in the rocket. We see the two clocks when the journey starts, and again when the journey is completed. According to a man on earth, the round trip to Barnard's star and back at one-third the speed of light will take 60 years. But according to the clock in the rocket, it only takes $56\frac{1}{2}$ years. The man in the rocket has aged, but he has aged $3\frac{1}{2}$ years less than the man left behind on earth.

In the following two pictures, we see the clocks again when the rocket is made to travel faster, at two-thirds the speed of light. According to a man on earth, the round trip to Barnard's star and back now takes 30 years. Let us suppose that the rocket makes this round trip twice. In fact, the first picture of the pair shows the rocket just beginning its second round trip; the last picture shows both clocks when the two round trips are completed. The clock on earth gives a total of 60 years for the double journey. But the clock in the rocket reads only $44\frac{1}{2}$ years. Again, the man on the rocket has aged, but he has aged less. Travelling at two-thirds the speed of light, this time he has aged $15\frac{1}{2}$ years less during the 60 years that have passed on earth.

felt—that is a rule of relativity. But all other movements can be felt; turning, or slowing down and stopping, or picking up speed. And however a man travels to Barnard's star and back, he has to do some of these.

However, there is no need to argue about such things theoretically. A more convincing argument is an experiment. And the experiment can now be done. There is a recent experiment which actually compares the passage of time in bodies moving at different speeds.

This experiment does not use distances measured in light-years, or speeds comparable with the speed of light. It is carried out in an ordinary laboratory, and it simply counts the ticks of a clock which is mounted at the edge of a spinning disc. The disc is only six inches across, and it spins first at 50 and later at 500 revolutions a second. The speed at the edge of the disc is therefore only 50 and later 500 miles an hour. These are small speeds, and the differences in the passage of time are very small indeed. They are far too small to be measured by an ordinary clock, so a clock of a special kind has to be used. We use the decay of a radioactive material as a clock; this can measure time to fractions of a thousand-millionth of a second.

Here is the disc with its radioactive clock. It works like this. There is a spot of radioactive iron in the centre of the disc, on the spindle. Round the edge of the disc is an absorber—the clock. This absorbs most of the rays which are given out each time that a radioactive atom decays. Beyond the disc is a counter which counts the few rays that get through the absorber. Each ray that the absorber captures is a tick of its clock. Each ray that gets through the absorber is a tick that the clock does *not* make. So the counter records those ticks that the moving clock did *not* make.

Next, the experiment is being mounted. The disc is screwed to the turntable that will spin it round, the machine is started, and the protective shield is lowered into place. The shield has nothing to do with the radioactivity. It is merely to guard the experimenter in case the spinning disc flies apart or breaks away from its support.

In the first experiment, the disc is run at a modest speed, namely at 50 revolutions a second. The radioactive clock at its edge is therefore making its round trips at about 50 miles an hour. The counter is registering the ticks which the radioactive clock does *not* make at this modest speed. At the end of 30 minutes (that is, after 90,000 round trips), they number 1017.

In the second experiment, the disc is speeded up; it is now spun at 500 revolutions a second. The radioactive clock at the edge makes the same round trips,

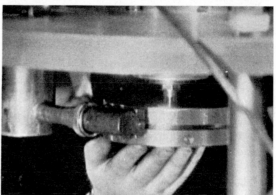

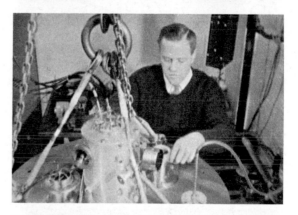

but ten times as fast; that is, at about 500 miles an hour. The counter again counts the ticks which the clock does *not* make in 30 minutes (that is, now, in 900,000 round trips).

This time they number 1064.

The difference between these two figures is 47. This is the measure of the difference in age, after 30 minutes, of a clock which has been moving at 50 miles an hour and a clock which has been moving at 500 miles an hour. The difference is almost at the limit of detection; the 47 missing ticks amount, in fact, to only one-half of a thousand-millionth of a second. A few years ago, we could not have detected such a tiny difference in time.

Yet the difference is real, and it is exactly as large as Einstein predicted. In 30 minutes, the clock moving at 500 miles an hour has made 47 fewer radioactive ticks than the clock moving at 50 miles an hour. All physical processes slow down in a moving body. The clock which has been moving faster has aged less. The difference is only one-half of a thousand-millionth of a second in 30 minutes. Yet it is as decisive as any difference that we could find in 60 years of travel between here and Barnard's star. For the principle is the same: the experiment that we

have seen is a Lilliput copy of the imaginary round trip to Barnard's star.

Einstein predicted all this 50 years ago. Only in the last year or two has it become possible to prove it in the laboratory. Relativity started as an idea, a piece of logic. It was never the sort of discovery that is stumbled on by accident in a corner of a laboratory.

Of course relativity is based on experiments, and it is confirmed by experiments. But it was, and it remains, a conception; a way of looking at the passing processes of nature. Einstein arrived at the conception by thinking. He saw that information cannot pass from place to place faster than light. It was a feat of imagination to conclude from this that space and time are related, and that the traveller in space carries his own time with him.

Science cannot exist without experiments, by which men check their ideas against facts. And equally science cannot exist without imagination, which suggests new ways of looking at the facts, new ways of looking at the world. Relativity is a fundamental way of looking at the world, and it has transformed our attitudes to life and our behaviour far beyond the boundaries of physics.

PART FIVE—LANGUAGE AND IMAGINATION

13

THE LANGUAGE OF ANIMALS

Language is often regarded as a special human gift, and in some ways it is. No animal has a language to express ideas; and even the ability to express emotions is very limited in animals. Yet language has one use which is shared by animals and humans: to communicate information.

When we speak of a language in animals, we do not mean only a language of sounds. An animal language may consist of movements, of gestures, and even of chemical signals. Any actions that animals use to pass information to one another make up a language. This is not a far-fetched meaning of the word 'language'—after all, we refer to human gestures as 'sign language'. So it is natural to recognise that animal gestures are also a language.

In this chapter we shall describe two animal languages: the language of bees, and the language of apes and monkeys. The dance of bees shows what accurate and complex information can be exchanged in a simple animal language. The gestures and calls of monkeys are far less precise, yet they form a language which can express something like human emotions. It is not really meaningful to ascribe emotions to lower animals—to say, for example, that bees are 'angry'. Bees can communicate exact information to one another, and nothing else. But monkeys do have emotions, and because their language expresses them, it is far closer to human language.

First, the language of bees. The pictures overleaf show a bee going through a dance which tells the other bees where to find food and what kind of food. The other bees are not crawling about at random. They are attentive and at times they join in the dance.

From time to time the dancing bee pauses to give some of the nectar it has gathered to one of the others. In this way, it tells the other bees from what sort of flowers the nectar was gathered. Chemical communication of this sort is quite common in the lower animals, and very effective. Female butterflies, for example, signal their position to the males by scent, sometimes for miles.

The dances of bees were first noticed as long ago as the eighteenth century. Even then it was understood that they lead to the gathering of food, and that a bee dances more vigorously, the richer the source of food it has found. At that time it was assumed that the bee that had found food simply excited the others by dancing, and then led them back to the source. It was not until the 1920's that Karl von Frisch, an Austrian zoologist, noticed that the dancer did not always go back to the source of food with the other bees. It soon became clear that when the forager bee dances, it is not merely saying that it has found food, and what kind. It is giving the other bees detailed information where the food is to be found.

Von Frisch studied the dances carefully, and he learned that there were two distinct types: the round dance and the wagtail dance. In the round dance, shown overleaf, the bee runs in a circle; and it reverses its direction from time to time. In the wagtail dance, the bee runs in a figure-of-eight. While it runs along the centre of the figure-of-eight, the bee waggles its body from side to side; and the dance gets its name from this characteristic movement.

In a long series of experiments, von Frisch showed that these dances tell the other bees both the distance

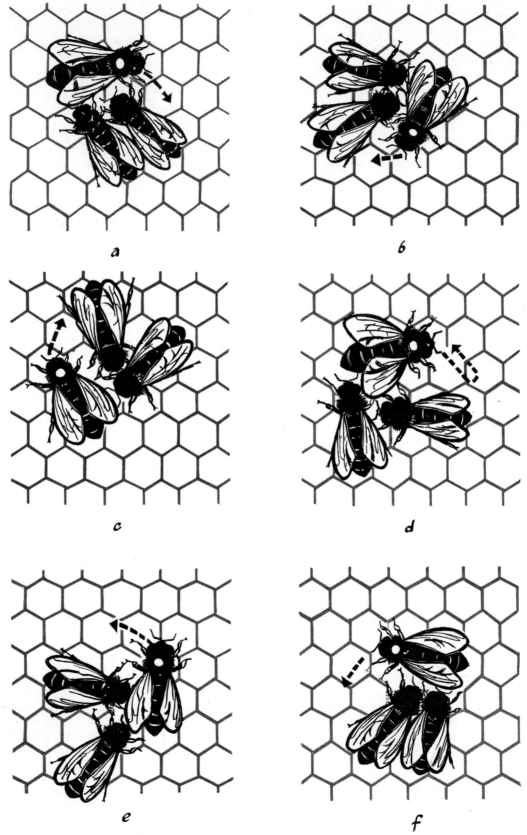

a

b

c

d

e

f

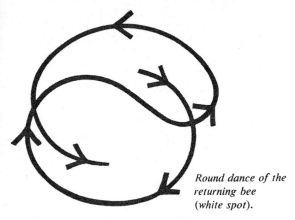

Round dance of the returning bee (white spot).

and the direction of the food. A forager bee does a round dance when it has found food fairly close to the hive, within 50 yards or so. For greater distances, the dance changes slightly and takes on some of the features of the wagtail dance. When the food is further away than about 100 yards, the dance becomes pure wagtail.

Thus the type of dance in itself tells the other bees whether the food is near or far. They then get more exact information from the speed and shape of the dance. The closer the food is, the faster the forager bee dances. If the food is 300 yards away, the bee dances 28 figures-of-eight a minute. If the food is 3,000 yards away, it dances only nine figures-of-eight a minute. And if the food is too far away to be worth gathering, the returning forager bee simply does not dance at all. By these signals (and there are other refinements) a forager bee on returning to the hive can tell the other bees how far off even distant food is to within a hundred yards or so.

Distance, however, is not all. The stay-at-home bees also want to know the direction of the food. This is simple if the dance takes place on the flat, outside the hive. The dancing bee simply points its straight run, along the centre of the figure-of-eight, in the right direction.

Things are more complicated and subtle when the dance takes place inside the hive, in the dark, on the vertical face of a honeycomb. The dancing bee now marks the direction of the food with respect to the sun. But there is no sun in the dark hive, so the bee puts gravity in place of the sun. That is, if the food is in the direction of the sun, the straight run along the centre of the figure-of-eight is made vertically upwards. If the food is in the opposite direction to the sun, the straight run is made vertically downwards. Other directions are shown by making the straight, wagtail run at the appropriate angle.

Bees use similar dances to tell a swarm where there is a good site for a nest. Scout bees go out to look for sites even before the swarm leaves the hive. When the scouts return, they dance on the surface of the swarm, and point the direction of a site in

much the same way as they point the direction of food. The scouts that have found the best site dance most vigorously, and so prompt other scouts (who are less enthusiastic about their finds) to follow their lead. In time the scouts all come to agree, and the swarm goes to nest at the agreed site. There is a case recorded, however, in which the scouts did not agree, and the swarm divided into two in mid-air.

The dance language of bees is remarkable, and a little fantastic. Yet it remains extremely limited. Bees can communicate their specialised information to one another very efficiently. But what they say, what they can say, is the minimum that they need in order to keep themselves alive and to keep their social structure intact. Their language is like a machine programme, automatic and predictable, to tell the hive what to do and no more.

We turn to our second theme: the language of apes and monkeys. This is a different kind of language; the signals in it are less mechanical, and do more to convey the monkey's state of mind. Charles Darwin called animal language of this kind the expression of the emotions. The emotions may not be exactly like our own; yet there is no doubt that some animals do make gestures of the same sort that we ourselves use to express emotions.

Consider the chimpanzee in these pictures, for example. What he appears to be feeling is surely

very similar to human curiosity. He investigates the mechanical toy in the first pair of pictures, and then the mysterious box in the second pair. When he opens the box, he is distinctly put out by what he finds inside. His gestures certainly appear to combine fear and anger.

The animals in the next set of pictures on the next page are rhesus monkeys.

The first four pictures show a male who is being provoked by a man outside the cage in a grotesque mask. The monkey is angry, and there are distinct phases in his show of anger. We see him in his threatening position, with his tail upright; after that he will jump at the wire. He will go through the same threat and leap many times. In the end, in the fourth picture, he turns his back in disgust, or is it boredom?

In the fifth picture the angry monkey is female. She also threatens; the hair bristles on her shoulders; but she holds her tail down and not up.

The threat posture and the raised tail are both gestures which form part of the language of the rhesus monkey. They communicate specific pieces of information to other rhesus monkeys. The position of the tail shows how agressive the monkey feels. When a monkey threatens, its feelings are always balanced between a desire to attack and a desire to flee. The position of the tail shows which desire is

stronger. When the tail is raised, the desire to attack is uppermost. The male in the pictures wants to attack. The female wants to run away, and her tail is lowered.

Other rhesus monkeys understand what these gestures mean; they form a language which is part of the monkey's social behaviour. Many of the gestures are developed from movements that the monkeys use socially. For example, in the sixth picture a mother is grooming her baby's fur. Grooming establishes a social bond between rhesus monkeys; a female will also groom a dominant male. Nearly always the subordinate animal grooms the dominant one.

The female in the second set of pictures over the page was reared by hand, and she is attached to humans. She is grooming her keeper's hand, to establish a social bond with him as she would with other monkeys. She does not take much notice of the other monkeys in the cage. In the last picture, she has stolen something from her keeper's pocket, and he is trying to get it back. Her grin is another characteristic gesture; it expresses fear, not pleasure.

All monkeys and apes communicate by gestures and movements, and they also communicate by sounds. For example, a group of baboons will scatter after a recording of their alarm call has been played to them. The alarm call is just a noise to human ears, but to the baboon its meaning is quite specific: Run! The baboon always obeys it.

All these specific gestures and noises make up the vocabulary of the language. The number of such words in the dictionary of a monkey or an ape is about twenty calls and twenty gestures—about forty words in all. This figure is fairly average for mammals and birds: those that have been studied have usually been found to have between twenty and fifty words in their vocabulary.

We are so familiar with the calls of birds that we tend to overlook their gestures. Yet gestures play an important part in their language also. In particular, the bright colours in the plumage of the birds are used to point their gestures. The male robin, for example, shows his red breast in the posture which he takes up to threaten other robins.

What is true of monkeys and robins is true of all the higher animals. Each species has a set of calls and gestures, and sometimes smells. And each one of these is a signal which conveys to other members of the species some information, usually about the signaller's state of mind.

So there is no doubt that it is meaningful to talk about the language of animals. They are, however,

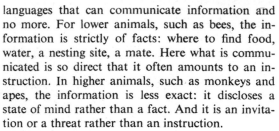

languages that can communicate information and no more. For lower animals, such as bees, the information is strictly of facts: where to find food, water, a nesting site, a mate. Here what is communicated is so direct that it often amounts to an instruction. In higher animals, such as monkeys and apes, the information is less exact: it discloses a state of mind rather than a fact. And it is an invitation or a threat rather than an instruction.

Human language contains these modes: it communicates both facts and states of mind. But human language also goes beyond them. It expresses ideas and concepts, and allows us to work with them in imagination in the mind. That is, language in humans is a tool for thinking as well as for communication. We shall see in the next chapter how the lack of language in this more imaginative sense limits the thinking of animals.

14

CAN ANIMALS THINK?

Anyone who has kept a pet knows that animals are intelligent. These pictures of a baboon who is matching geometrical shapes show the level of an animal's intelligence. The baboon is more intelligent than a cat or a dog, but not much more.

The baboon is shown a shape, and his task is to pick a shape like it. The shapes are geometrical: cubes, discs, cylinders. The baboon does not always get the right shape at once, but he does so in the end, and gets his reward. He does about as well as a child would do between the ages of two and three

years. A child and a baboon understand how to choose between one shape and another.

The ability to choose distinguishes the baboon from the bees in the last chapter. The dance of the forager bee and the response of the other bees are automatic, like the flight of a moth towards the light. The moth does not choose to fly towards the light; it does so mechanically. And like the moth, the bees are not thinking. But the baboon choosing shapes is. He is working with ideas, even though he can only choose a shape that he actually sees.

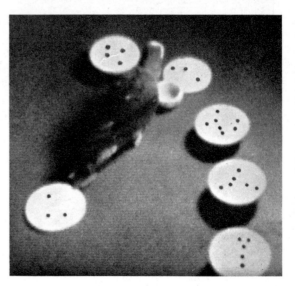

Animals can have more subtle ideas than shape. They have some idea of number. In Germany, Otto Köhler has shown that animals can even count, if the number of things to count is small. His experiments are fascinating, and show how far animals can indeed think.

Köhler put several bowls in front of a bird or a squirrel. Each bowl had a cover, on which were a number of dots arranged irregularly. The pictures show some of the covers. The animals were shown a cover with, say, three dots on it. This meant that food was to be found in the bowl with three dots on its cover. If the animal chose the correct bowl with no mistake, it got the food as reward. In these pictures, a parrot is seen making its choice correctly.

The significance of these experiments lies in this: the dots are arranged differently on the cover that

the animal is shown and on the cover that conceals the food. If the arrangements were the same, the animal could merely recognise the pattern of dots. But as the pictures show, the arrangements are quite different. So the only sign by which the cover over the food can be recognised is the *number* of dots. The animal must have an idea of number; it must be able to match numbers. Otherwise it could not make the correct choice.

Experiments of this sort show that birds and animals can match numbers up to about seven. They are in fact able to recognise seven dots in any arrangement. And dots of quite different shapes do not confuse them. The squirrel in the pictures on the next page was faced with six dots that had been enlarged to irregular splodges, yet it was able to find the right bowl at once.

not yet proved that animals can actually count. This is not quite the same thing. An animal might be able to indentify the number of dots in a group without counting them one by one. (We shall see that humans do just this with numbers up to seven.) But the next experiment shows conclusively that birds can also count.

These pictures show the arrangement of the experiment. There are seven covered bowls containing in all seven seeds. The seeds are distributed irregularly—perhaps none in the first bowl, two in the second, one in the third bowl, four in the fourth, and none in the rest.

Next, the squirrel is set a different kind of problem. Four of the covers now have the same number of dots on them—in this picture, four dots. The fifth cover has a different number of dots, and it is this fifth cover that hides the food. As the picture shows, the squirrel can pick out the number that is different, and learn to choose it. This is a more subtle choice than in the first experiment. It requires the animal to recognise and compare several numbers. That is much more searching than the task that the baboon was set.

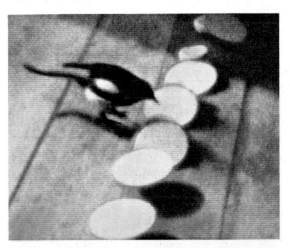

So far, we have proved that animals have an idea of number. They can recognise small numbers, can match them and choose between them. But we have

The bird is trained to look for seven seeds, and it works through the bowls picking them out. When it has found seven, it does not look for any more. Here the bird has found three seeds in the fourth bowl and four in the fifth, and at once it ignores the remaining bowls. It can undoubtedly count up to seven, seed by seed.

The parrot in the pictures on the right is even more advanced; it can look for any specified number of seeds. First the bird is shown a card with a number of dots on it—in this case, three dots. Then it goes to find just that number of seeds in the bowls. When it has found the specified number, it does not look any further.

These experiments show with great elegance that animals have a sense of number, and they are able to count. They can grasp and use one of the basic ideas of mathematics: the idea of number—at any rate, up to the number seven. This is unexpected, and remarkable.

Yet these experiments tax the mathematical ability of animals to the limit. Even the most intelligent of chimpanzees cannot be taught to multiply. He can count numbers, but he cannot work with them. And he cannot work with them because he has no names for them.

It is the names, the symbols, which enable us to carry ideas in our heads and work with them. We do not work with dots. We use figures or other symbols, which are names for numbers. Without these names, our arithmetic would not be much better than a bird's.

In fact, seven is about the limit also of a man's ability to recognise numbers, if he is not allowed to operate with them by an arithmetical method. To grasp more than about seven dots, for example, a man must be able to arrange them in groups in his mind, or count them singly. (Here he is better than a bird: he can count beyond seven.) That is, a man can recognise 'threeness', 'fourness', and so on, up to 'sevenness' or thereabouts. Beyond that, he can usually recognise a pattern of more than seven dots only if it is regular enough to be broken into groups. If it is, and he can break it into groups that he can recognise, then he adds up the groups in his head by using their names. And that is just the kind of arithmetical method which an animal is not able to use.

A simple experiment makes the point. A man sits in front of a dark screen; from time to time, a set of bright dots is flashed on the screen. The dots are arranged at random, so that the man cannot see them as separate groups. And they are flashed for a tenth of a second only, so that he has no time to count them singly.

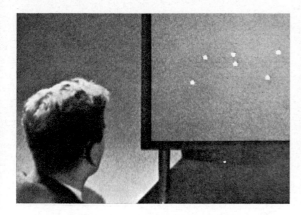

GUESS: 6

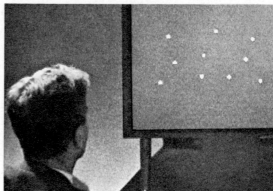

GUESS: 11

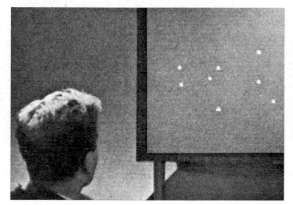

GUESS: 7

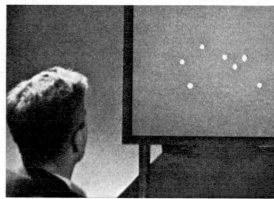

GUESS: 7

The result of a run of such flashes is shown in the pictures. The number under each picture was the number of dots which the man guessed he had seen. He turned out to be exactly the average case. He guessed right whenever the number of dots shown him was seven or fewer, and guessed wrong whenever it was more than seven.

The point of this experiment is not to show that a man cannot count beyond seven in a tenth of a second. It is to show that our human ability is almost as limited as a bird's if we do not operate with named concepts. The idea of 'fourness' is not enough in itself; we need the name 'four' or the symbol 4 if we are to work with the number in our heads. The man in the experiment was prevented, by the arrangement and the timing, from using such relations as $4+4=8$.

And he found that, without these, he could not recognise 'eightness' any better than a bird can.

This is the theme of this chapter. Human beings can only work with ideas because (and when) they have a language for them. The names or symbols for numbers are part of this human language; and so are the names of all other concepts and ideas. For human beings, language is more than a means of communication. Language is the tool of ideas.

Köhler's experiments show that animals do have ideas. And of course they have ideas about other things than numbers, too. But the ideas do not take them far, because they cannot work with them in their heads. They cannot call them up by name, to put them together and draw fresh conclusions from them. We end this chapter with a description which illustrates vividly what it means for an animal not to be able to put ideas together in the mind.

The subject of this experiment is, after man, the most intelligent of all animals. He is a chimpanzee, and it is safe to assume that no other animal would do better than he in the same test. The chimpanzee has been taught to do something quite skilful—to put out a fire with water. The final set of pictures in this chapter show him doing it. When the chimpanzee sees the fire lit, he draws a cup of water from the drum and pours it over the flames. In this way he reaches a reward of food, which is beyond the flames. This is a complicated series of operations, but the chimpanzee can see the point of them; they lead sensibly to his reward beyond the flames, and nothing else does. So long as the conditions are not changed, the chimpanzee will go on putting out fires very neatly.

The pictures also show the same problem in a new setting. The stove in which the fire is lit is now on a raft floating on a lake. The drum with water in it is on another raft, connected to the first by a ladder which acts as a rickety gangway. Before the fire is lit, the chimpanzee is given every opportunity for getting to know that the stuff he is floating on is the same stuff that comes out of the tap on the drum.

We actually see him playing with it.

But when the time comes, the chimpanzee cannot make use of his knowledge. The fire is lit, and the chimpanzee, sitting beside it, sees his reward beyond the flames. He only has to put out the fire. Yet instead of simply reaching over the side of the raft for his cupful of water, he goes through an elaborate manoeuvre. He crosses the ladder to the other raft, fills the cup from the drum, and brings it back again to put out the fire. The operation is difficult. Coming back across the ladder, the chimpanzee even has to carry the cup in his teeth. The way he sets about putting out the fire is vastly more complicated than filling the cup from the lake. But it uses the stuff he was taught to use, out of the drum; and he cannot think of using (or even trying to use) any other stuff.

The step that the chimpanzee failed to make was to connect the water in the drum with the water in the lake. He had every opportunity for doing so, yet he could not relate the two. The water in the lake and the water in the drum were not the same thing to him. He had no idea of 'wateriness' as a property shared by the stuff that the rafts were floating on and the stuff in the drum. And it did not occur to him to experiment—at least to try the stuff at his feet.

At bottom, the chimpanzee is behaving like the baby at the beginning of this book, for whom the toy did not exist when it was out of sight. Every new object, and different appearances of the same object, are new sets of sense impressions. As a baby grows up, it learns to sort out these sense impressions, to recognise likenesses and differences, and to imagine objects even when they cannot be seen. In this way, the baby learns that water is water, whether it is in a drum with a tap, in a lake with rafts floating on it, or in the bath. A chimpanzee never learns some of these things. Even when he has the experiences, he does not have the words which can put different experiences together in the mind. To take a phrase

from the beginning of this book, the chimpanzee never enters the gateway to the imagination.

And because the chimpanzee is not able to imagine, he does not even *experiment*. This is the fundamental shortcoming in his behaviour: that he did not even try the water in the lake. Contrast his mechanical behaviour with the game of the children at the beginning of the book. They can imagine how to catch an imaginary bird with an imaginary rope in an imaginary hole, dug with an imaginary shovel.

Dig—dig a big hole
Now let me dig the hole—
No—no—you're not—no—I dig the hole—
The shovel's too big for you—I have to dig the
   hole—
Wanna hold the rope?
Yes
Well then hold the rope the right way—
You're not holding it the right way
What?
It's supposed to curl right up—
What?
It has to twirl right up—
I can't hear you—
Stop in the hole—

These children would have no difficulty in recognising that water is water in two different places. They can carry ideas in their minds, and put them together, far away from the objects they refer to. Language makes it possible for them to have this imagination, which will lead them to experiments that a chimpanzee cannot think of.

A bird can count numbers, a baboon can compare shapes, a chimpanzee can grasp that a flame will not scorch after he has poured water on it. These are ideas: simple ideas, yet quite like human ideas. What keeps them so far short of the ideas of Shakespeare and Einstein? The animal cannot develop its ideas, it cannot carry them in the mind, put one idea beside another, do imaginary things with them. The animal has no language for all this; and language is the tool of ideas.

15

THE VISION OF OUR AGE

This book began at the birth of a child, and traced its development until it enters 'the gateway to imagination and reason'. This is the stage when the child can manipulate objects in thought as well as with its hands: when it can make images of them. The child has little knowledge yet, in the ordinary sense of the word; but it has the mental equipment to learn and create knowledge. Once a child can make images, it can also reason, and build for itself a coherent picture of the world that is more than separate bundles of sense impressions.

We have just seen that when a child enters 'the gateway to imagination', it leaves all animals behind. Before it learns to make images, a young human develops in much the same way as a young animal. Children and animals alike have to learn to co-ordinate their various senses and to recognise objects. But after that, animals fall behind. They have no power of imagination. That is, they cannot carry images in the mind; and without imagery, without an inner language, they cannot manipulate ideas.

The theme of imagination runs through this book. We have examined some of the great achievements of science and seen that they are imaginative ideas. Science does not merely plod on like a surveyor, laboriously mapping a stretch of country, square mile by square mile. Of course nature must be surveyed, and very laborious that is at times; but the survey is not the end. The great moments in science come when men of imagination sit down and think about the findings—when they recreate the landscape of nature under the survey.

Science must be solidly grounded in fact and in experiment. But a blind search for experimental facts is not enough; it could never have discovered the theory of relativity. Science is a way of looking at things, an insight, a vision. And the theories of science are the underlying patterns that this way of looking at the world reveals. Many of the patterns are unexpected even at the simplest beginnings. (For example, common sense would not even have expected to find that stars and human beings are put together from the same basic building bricks of matter.) And the more unexpected the pattern, the greater the feat of imagination that is needed to see it for the first time.

What place have these imaginative ideas of science in our daily thoughts? Science and technology have transformed the physical world we live in; but have they yet had much effect on thought? Many people even dislike the ideas of science, and feel that they are abstract and mechanical. They reject science because they fear that it is in some way inhuman.

This book shows that science is as much a creation of the human imagination as art is. Science and art are not opposites; they spring from the same human impulses. In this last chapter, we shall examine their relations to one another, in the past and today. In particular, we shall see how both enter and combine into the way man in the twentieth century sees the world: the vision of our age. For this purpose, we shall include personal statements about their own work by an artist, an architect, a scientist, and a writer.

The artist is the sculptor Eduardo Paolozzi. The group of pictures show him in his studio, then one of his sculptures being cast in the foundry, then one of his finished sculptures called *San Sebastian*—with a jet engine standing in the background—and finally another recent work.

This is what Eduardo Paolozzi had to say about his work and the world for which it is made.

'I am a sculptor, which means that I make images. As a sculptor I was taught at the Slade the classical idea of being an artist. The best one could do would be to emulate Victorian ideals and to work in a studio executing portraits or monuments.

'But there has been a rejection now of the classical idea of tracing art out of art, which is in a way a sort of death process leading to the provincial gallery, with the atmosphere of the death-watch beetle—a gilt-edged, sure-thing idea of art.

'In this century we have found a new kind of freedom—an opening up of what is possible to the artist as well as to the scientist. So I don't make copies of conventional works of art. I'm not working for Aunt Maud; I'm trying to do things which have a meaning for us living today, that is, mechanisms and throwaway objects. To me they are beautiful, as my children are beautiful, though in a different way. I think they are different definitions of beauty.

'I haven't got any desire to make a sculpture of my children; but a wheel, a jet engine, a bit of a machine is beautiful, if one chooses to see it in that way. It's even more beautiful if one can improve it, by incorporating it in one's iconography. For instance, something like the jet engine is an exciting image if you're a sculptor. I think it can quite fairly sit in the mind as an art image as much as an Assyrian wine jar. I think it's a beautifully logical image, in the sense that anything in its delicate structure, with its high precision standards, has got a reason, almost in a way like human anatomy.

'My *San Sebastian* was a sort of God I made out of my own necessity: a very beautiful young man being killed by arrows, which has a great deal of symbolism in it. I think this is a good thing for young artists to identify themselves with, in a way that doing the Madonna and Child may not be a thing they can identify themselves with. It has two legs, which are decorated columns, it has a rather open, symbolical square torso, with disguised, warped, twisted, mechanic elements. Then the final element is a sort of drum with a space cut in the middle.

'What I feel about using the human diagram is that it points up in a more specific way the relationship between man and technology. There isn't any point in having a good idea in sculpture unless there is some kind of plastic or formal organisation. So I don't reproduce the jet engine, I transform it. And I use the wheel a lot in my sculpture as a symbol,

as a quickly read symbol, of the man-made object. This also refers back to my crude peasant idea of science, which is that the wheel gives the idea of man being able to get off the ground. The wheel to me is important, and the clock. I think this is very significant—I find the clock moving because I find modern science moving. I see it as a sort of heroic symbolism.

'In the last fifty years, science seems to be the outstanding leading direction, the most considerable direction that man has taken. It is trying continually to go beyond what was possible till that very moment. I think there is a possibility in what I call, crudely, higher science, a tremendous possibility of man being free. And I think it can give me a certain kind of moral strength, in the sense that art can move into a similar category of freedom. In my sculpture I am trying to speak for the way people are freeing themselves from traditional ideas. I'm a sculptor and so I put these ideas into images. If I do this well they'll be heroic images, ones that will survive and ones which other ages will recognise. Image making gives me the sense of freedom in a way that nothing else can.'

A word to which Paolozzi returns several times is 'free'. He feels that science frees man, from his conventions, from the restrictions of his environment, from his own fears and self-doubts. If this is true, then man has gained this growing freedom by imagination: in science, by imagining things that have not yet happened. Paolozzi wants to communicate the same sense of growing freedom in the images of his sculpture. He wants people to feel that they are heroic images.

Science and art are both imaginative activities, and they present two sides of the imagination. The two sides have often tried and often failed to come together, in the past and in recent time. This chapter itself, and this book, is an attempt to help bring them together. Paolozzi's work is also an attempt to bring them together, in a different language. He uses the everyday products of technology (the stamped shapes in the first picture, for example) as the raw material of his art, because they seem to him as natural and expressive in modern civilisation as the human body itself.

It is interesting to look at the two sides of the human imagination in an earlier civilisation. We have evidence for them, long even before writing was invented. These paintings, in the caves of Lascaux in southern France, are at least twenty thousand years old. They are the most famous and the finest examples of art from the Stone Age. The word 'art' is not out of place, and yet it is most unlikely that these pictures were created in the same spirit as

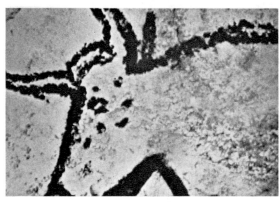

classical art. The caves of Lascaux were not a Stone Age art gallery that people came to visit. Art of this kind was an integral part of the civilisation of Stone Age man.

The Lascaux paintings are a product of one side of the imagination of the men who lived twenty thousand years ago. This picture shows a product of the other side of their imagination. It is a tool: a harpoon, cut from bone. It has barbs, like a modern fish hook, to stop it from being pulled out when it lodges in an animal.

The next picture shows a tool again, and of a subtler kind. It does not look as impressive as the harpoon, yet it is in fact a more far-sighted invention. For it is a tool for making tools: it is a stone graver of the sort that must have been used to cut the barbs

in the harpoon. The men who invented this were able to think beyond the immediate needs of the day—killing an animal, cutting it up, scraping its hide. When they invented a tool for making tools (today we should call that a machine-tool) they took a new step of the imagination.

What is the link between paintings on the wall of a cave, and primitive tools made of bone and flint? Separated as we are by twenty thousand years from the men who created both, we can only speculate. But we are surely right in speculating that the paint-

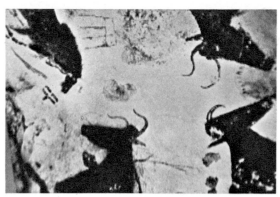

ings served some purpose other than mere decoration. Look at another Lascaux painting. It represents three bulls and (probably) a boar. A bull is being struck by a spear with barbs—a spear like the one that we have seen. This is plainly a hunting scene. Many of the other cave paintings show similar scenes. The painters were constantly preoccupied with hunting. This is why most authorities agree that the paintings were some kind of magic, and were intended to help the hunter to dominate the animal before the hunt started.

Unhappily, 'magic' is one of those words ('instinct' is another) that does not really explain anything. It merely says that we do not know the explanation. What kind of magic were the painters making? What did they feel they were doing for the hunters? How did they think that they were helping them to dominate the hunted animal?

Here I will give my personal view. I think that the paintings helped the men who painted them, and the men who lived in the caves with them, to conquer their fear of the hunted animal. A bull was (and is) a dangerous beast, and out in the open there would not be much time to think about him. By drawing him you become familiar with him, get used to the idea of meeting and hunting him, and imagine ways in which he can be outwitted. The close-up makes the bull familiar to you; and the familiar is never as frightening as the unknown.

It is not far-fetched here to draw an analogy with modern methods of training. Consider, for example, the training of spacemen. They have to face a frightening situation, in which what they fear is simply the unfamiliar and unknown. They will not survive if they panic; they will do the wrong thing. So a long and life-like training programme is designed to make them familiar in advance with every situation that they are likely to encounter. The spaceman's training is more than a matter of simply learning to press the right buttons. It is also a psychological preparation for the unknown.

I believe that the Stone Age cave paintings were also a psychological preparation for the unknown.

101

CARL A. RUDISILL LIBRARY
LENOIR RHYNE COLLEGE

They helped the Stone Age hunters to dominate their psychological environment, just as flint and bone tools helped them to dominate their physical environment. That is the connecting link between the two. Both are tools, that is, instruments which man uses to free himself and to overcome the limitations of nature. It was Benjamin Franklin who first defined man as 'the tool-making animal'. He was right, and the tools are mental as well as physical.

We move forward now many thousand years, to a time and place where the two sides of the human imagination worked more closely together than ever before, and perhaps ever since. The pictures on the right come from Athens of the fifth century B.C. The men who built this city had suddenly burst out of the confines of the cave and come into the light of freedom. Their civilisation recognised that man's most powerful tool in the command of nature is the human mind. The Greeks named their city, and the great temple of the Parthenon in it, after the goddess of wisdom, Athene. Light and reason, logic and imagination together dominated their civilisation.

Greek architecture, for example, has a strong mathematical basis, yet it never appears stiff and mechanical. Look at the Parthenon, as perfect a creation in architecture as man has made; and it is dominated by a precise sense of numbers. Numbers had a mystical significance for the Greeks (Pythagoras made them almost into a religion) and this expressed itself in all they did.

The Parthenon has 8 columns along the front and 17 along each side. That to the Greeks was the ideal proportion. The number of columns along each side of a temple should be twice the number along the front, plus one more. No Greek architect would have built otherwise.

Numbers that are perfect squares seemed to the Greeks equally fascinating and beautiful. The Parthenon is 4 units wide and 9 units long; for 4 is the square of 2, and 9 is the square of 3—the two smallest squares. The ratio of height to width along the front of the building is also 4 to 9; and so is the ratio of the thickness of the columns to the distance between them.

Yet all this arithmetic is not a dead ritual. The Greeks found it exciting because they found it in natural objects. To them, it expressed the mystery of nature, her inner structure. Numbers were a key to the way the world is put together: this was the belief that inspired their science and their art together.

So the Parthenon is nowhere merely a set of mathematical relations. The architect is guided by the numbers, but he is never hidebound by them.

His plan begins with arithmetic, but after that the architect himself has taken command of the building, and has given it freedom, lightness and rhythm. For example, the end columns are closer to their neighbours than are the other columns; and the end columns are also a little thicker. This is to make the building compact, to make it seem to look inwards at the corners. And all the columns lean slightly inwards, in order to give the eye (and therefore the building) a feeling of upward movement and of lightness.

The pictures on the right are of the Erictheum. It stands close to the Parthenon, but is less famous. Perhaps that is because the Erictheum is less monumental, more slender, more delicate in its whole conception. Yet the mathematics is still there. The porch of the Erictheum, for instance, is designed on the 'golden section'. That is, the canopy has the same proportion to the base as the base has to the human figures which support the canopy. The golden section was a mathematical relation which was based on nature: on the proportions of the human body.

The human figures which support the canopy are made to seem in movement; two rest on the right foot, two on the left. Everywhere in the Erictheum there is the feeling of movement. The different levels of the building are joined together with suppleness and rhythm. This is what the Erictheum expresses in architecture: an almost musical sense of rhythm. And this reminds us that Pythagoras prided himself, rightly, on having discovered the mathematical structure of the musical scale.

The fusion of the mathematical order with the human, of reason with imagination, was the triumph of Greek civilisation. The artists accepted the mathematics, and the mathematicians did not resent the architects imposing their individuality on the mathematical framework. It was a civilisation which expressed itself in the way things were put together—buildings, ideas, society itself. Greek architecture survives to illustrate this, perhaps better than any other record.

All architecture must begin with technical efficiency. Walls have to stand up, roofs have to keep the rain out. So an architect can never be unpractical, as can a painter or a sculptor. He cannot be content with the mere look of the thing. The side of the human imagination which made the Stone Age tools cannot be left out. But a bad architect can play it down, and can take the practical for granted, as a painter takes his canvas for granted.

The strength of the best architecture today is that it does not despise the practical purposes of buildings. It does not hide the structure and function under merely elegant decoration. Structure and function in modern buildings play the same fundamental part as numbers in Greek architecture. They form

the framework on which the architect imposes his individual imagination. And he does not pretend that the framework is not there.

Our next personal statement comes from a famous architect, Eero Saarinen. He was born in Finland but built most of his great buildings in America. The pictures below show the building that he did not live to finish, the TWA Air Terminal at Idlewild Airport in New York. The lines of the building are very dramatic, and the form is consciously mathematical and aerodynamic. The question is: Is the bold, flying shape necessary, or is it a romantic artifice without a true function? I discussed this with Eero Saarinen during the building, and this is how he replied.

'To really answer your question, I would have to go a little bit back, and talk philosophically about architecture. As you know, we all, in architecture, have been working in this modern style, and certain principles have grown up within it. The basic principles are really three. There is the functional part. There is the structural part, honestly expressing the structure of the building. And the third thing is that the building must be an expression of our time. In other words, the technology of our time must be expressed in a building.

'Now those are the principles that we are all agreed on—the principles that one might have said ten years ago were the only principles. I think since that time more thought and maybe some more principles have grown up. I would say one of these additional principles, one which I believe in, is that where buildings have a truly significant purpose they should also express that purpose.'

Function and purpose were not the same thing in Saarinen's mind. The TWA Air Terminal has a clear function: to handle passengers into and out of aeroplanes. But for Saarinen, it also had a deeper purpose: from here people were to fly, and he wanted to give them the sense of freedom and adventure which flying has for earth-bound men. The vaulted shapes of the building were well-conceived as structures, but they were meant to be more: their aerodynamic and birdlike look was to express what Saarinen called the purpose—the sense of going off to fly. And the long spurs reaching out from the building show that it is not something self-contained, an end-point. They suggest entering the building and leaving it, which is of course what the passengers do.

Eero Saarinen went on:

'The last thing that I've become convinced of, and I'm not the only one, there are many others, is that once you've set the design, it must create an architectural unity. The idea of the barrel vaults making the roof of the Air Terminal building is carried through in all the details, even the furnishings.

'Basically architecture is an art, though it is half-way between an art and a science. In a way it straddles the two. I think to a large degree the motivating force in the designing of architecture comes from the arts side. If you ask, Are these curves and everything derived from mathematics? the answer is No. They are sympathetic with the forces within the vaults, which is mathematical, but there are so many choices which one has, and these really come from the aesthetic side.

'To me architecture is terribly important because it is really an expression of the whole age. After we're dead and gone, we're going to be judged by our architecture, by the cities we leave behind us, just as other times have been. What man does with architecture in his own time gives him belief in himself and in the whole period. Architecture is not just a servant of society, in a sense it's a leader of society.'

Architecture straddles art and science. That statement is true of the Greek architecture of two thousand years ago as well as of the architecture of today. In this, the Greek imagination is close to our own. The Greeks were preoccupied with the idea of structure; and we have seen in this book that the idea of structure is also central to modern science. Like the Greeks, the modern scientist is always looking at the way things are put together, the bones beneath the skin. How often in this book have we used such phrases as 'the architecture of matter'!

For example, the Greeks invented the idea of the atom as the smallest unit of matter from which everything in the world is built. Plato thought there were five kinds of atom, and he pictured them as the five regular solids of geometry. The first four were the atoms of the four kinds of matter: earth, air, fire, and water; one of these is shown in the first picture below. The fifth was the universe itself, the unity of the other four—we still call it the quintessence; it is shown, as Plato imagined it, in the second picture.

This conception is fantastic, and the atoms it pictures have no relation to the facts. And yet the fanciful pictures are a first attempt to solve, imaginatively, the same problems of structure and behaviour that the modern physicist faces. The Greek conception and the modern theories about atoms are both attempts to explain the bewildering complexity of the observable world in terms of an underlying, unifying order. Greek scientific theories are now only of historical interest. Yet before the Greeks, no one had thought about the world in this way at all. Without them, there would have been no modern science. It was the Greeks who first formulated the problems that modern science tries to answer.

Our third personal statement comes from a physicist: Professor Abdus Salam, of the Imperial College of Science in London. He describes some modern ideas about atoms. They are a long way from Plato's regular solids; yet, as Professor Salam points out, that is where they started. Here is what Salam said.

'I am a theoretical physicist, and we theoretical physicists are engaged on the following problem. We would like to understand the entire complexity of inanimate matter in terms of as few fundamental concepts as possible. This is not a new quest. It's the quest which humanity has had from the beginning of time—the Greeks were engaged on it. They conceived of all matter as being made up of fire, water, earth and air. The Arabs had their ideas about it too. Scientists have been worried about this all through the centuries. The nearest man came to solving this problem was in 1931 when, through the work done in the Cavendish Laboratory in Cambridge, we believed that all matter consisted of just two particles—electrons and protons—and all forces of nature were essentially of two kinds, the gravitational force and the electrical force.

'Now we know that this view of 1931 was erroneous. Since that time the number of particles has increased to thirty, and the number of elementary forces to four. In addition to the electrical and gravitational forces, we now believe that there are two other types of force, both nuclear—one extremely strong, and the other extremely weak. And the task we are engaged on is to try to reduce this seeming complexity to something which is simple and elementary.

'Now the type of magic which we use in order to solve our problem is first to rely on the language which we use throwing up ideas of its own. The language which we use in our subject is the language of mathematics, and the best example of the language throwing up ideas is the work of Dirac in 1928. He started with the idea that he would like to combine the theory of relativity and the theory of quantum mechanics. He proceeded to do this by writing a mathematical equation, which he solved. And to his

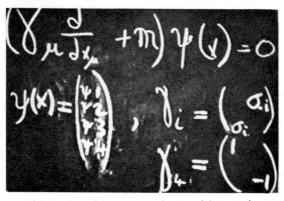

astonishment, and to everyone's astonishment, it was found that this equation described not only the particles—electrons and protons—which Dirac had designed the equation for, but also particles of so-called anti-matter—anti-electrons, anti-protons.

'So in one stroke Dirac had increased the number of particles to twice the number. There are the particles of matter, there are the particles of anti-matter. In a sense, of course, this produces simplicity too, because when I speak of thirty particles, really fifteen of them are particles and fifteen of them are anti-particles. The power of mathematics as a language that suggests and leads you on to something, which we in theoretical physics are very familiar with, reminds me of the association of ideas which follows when possibly a great poet is composing poetry. He has a certain rhyme, and the rhyme itself suggests the next idea, and so on. That is one type of way in which invention comes about.

'The second type of idea which we use to solve

our problems is the idea of making a physical picture. A very good illustration is the work of the Japanese physicist Yukawa in 1935. Yukawa started to ponder on the problem of the attractive force between two protons, and he started with the following picture. Suppose there are two cricketers, who have a cricket ball, and they decide to exchange the ball. One throws the ball and the other catches it, perhaps. Suppose they want to go on exchanging the ball, to and fro, between them. Then the fact that they must go on exchanging the ball means that they must keep within a certain distance of each other.

'The result is the following picture. If one proton emits something which is captured by the second one, and the second one emits something which is captured by the first one, then the fact that they have to capture, emit, re-absorb constantly means that they will remain within a certain distance of each other. And someone who cannot see this intermediate object, this ball, the object we call the meson, will think that these two protons have an attractive force between them. This was Yukawa's way of explaining the attractive force between two elementary particles.

'The result of Yukawa's work was that he predicted that there do exist such particles which play the role of intermediate objects. And he predicted that such particles would have a mass about three hundred times that of electrons. Yukawa made this prediction in 1935. In 1938 these particles were discovered, and we now firmly believe that the forces of nature, all forces of nature, are transmitted by this type of exchange of intermediary particles.

'Now so far I have been talking about our methods, but what is really important are our aims. Our aim in all this is to reduce the complexity of the thirty elementary particles and the four fundamental forces into something which is simple and beautiful. And to do this what we shall most certainly need is a break from the type of ideas which I have expressed —a complete break from the past, and a new and audacious idea of the type which Einstein had at the beginning of this century. An idea of this type comes perhaps once in a century, but that is the sort of thing which will be needed before this complexity is reduced to something simple.'

The ideas put forward by Salam are vivid. But more than the specific ideas, we are interested here in his description of science itself. For him, science is the attempt to find in the complexity of nature something which is simple and beautiful. This is quite different from the usual view that science collects facts and uses them to make machines and gadgets. Salam sees science as a truly imaginative activity, with a poetic language of its own. This is an arresting point that Salam made: that the mathematics in science is a poetic language, because it spontaneously throws up new images, new ideas.

Science can learn from the language of poetry, and literature can learn from the language of science. Here we bring in our fourth contributor. He is Lawrence Durrell, who wrote the four famous books which make up *The Alexandria Quartet*. In this four-fold novel, space and time are treated in an unusual way, and Durrell began by talking about this.

'I was hunting for a form which I thought might deliver us from the serial novel, and in playing around with the notions of relativity it seemed to me that if Einstein were right some very curious by-products of his idea would emerge. For example, that truth was no longer absolute, as it was to the Victorians, but was very provisional and very much subject to the observer's view.

'And while I felt that many writers had been questing around to find a new form, I think they hadn't succeeded. I don't know of course, I've only read deeply in French. There may well be Russian or German novels which express this far better than I have.

'But they hadn't expressed what I think Einstein would call the 'discontinuity' of our existence, in the sense that we no longer live (if his reality is right) serially, historically, from youth to middle age, to death; but in every second of our lives is packed, in capsule form, a sort of summation of the whole. That's one of the by-products of relativity that I got.

'In questing around for a means of actually presenting this in such an unfamiliar form as a novel, I borrowed a sort of analogy, perhaps falsely, from the movie camera. I'd been working with one, and it seemed to me that when the camera traverses across a field and does a pan shot, it's a historic shot in the sense that it goes from A to B to C to D. And if it starts with a fingernail and backtracks until you get a whole battlefield, that seemed to me a spatialisation. It was rooted in the time sequence that it was spatialising; it was still enlarging spatially.

'I tried to mix these two elements together, and see what would happen to ordinary human characters in what is after all a perfectly old-fashioned type of novel—an ordinary novel, only not serial. I found, somewhat to my own surprise, that I was getting a kind of stereoscopic narrative, and getting a kind of stereophonic notion of character. This excited me so much that I finished it and tried to add the dimension of time by moving the whole thing forward—you know, "read our next issue"—five years later. And there it is, ready for the critics to play with.'

Here are Lawrence Durrell's answers to some questions about his work:

Q. You said that you got from relativity the feeling that truth was provisional, or at least depended very much on the observer.

A. Well, the analogy again is the observer's position in time and space. It's so to speak the fulcrum out of which his observation grows, and in that sense it is not an absolute view, it's provisional. The subject matter is conditioned by the observer's point of view.

Q. You're really making the point that the most important thing that relativity says is that there are no absolutes?

A. I was saying, most important for me. I think that any average person who's not a mathematician would assume that that was probably the most important part of it.

Q. I want to recall another phrase that you've just used. You said of your novel that 'after all it's a perfectly old-fashioned novel'. Now I don't feel that. I feel that your novel could have been written at no time but in the twentieth century.

A. Yes, in that sense certainly. But I was trying to distinguish between the form which, I believe, if it has come off at all, is original, and the content. When I was building the form I did something new. I said to myself, this is the shape: there are three sides of space, one of time. How do I shift this notion into such an unusual domain as the novel? And at the back of my mind I wondered whether we in the novel couldn't escape our obsession with time only.

Q. Your dimensions, as it were, deepen out each character as a recession in space. You show how different he becomes when he is seen by someone else from another point.

A. Stereoscopically, you see.

Q. I want to ask you a crucial question. Do you feel that the kind of inspiration that you've drawn from the scientific idea of relativity here is valid for everyone? That we can all in some way make a culture which combines science and the arts?

A. Surely a balanced culture must do that. And I think all the big cultures of the past have never made very rigid distinctions. Also I think that the very great artists, the sort of universal men, Goethe for example, are as much scientists as artists. When Goethe wasn't writing poetry he was nourishing himself on science.

Q. We can't expect everybody to be a Goethe, so how are we going to unify what is obviously different—the sense of what the artist is doing and the sense of what the scientist is doing?

A. I think by understanding that in every generation the creative part of the population feels called upon to try and attack this mysterious riddle of what we're doing, and to give some account of themselves. We're up against a dualism, because some people have more intelligence and less emotion, and vice versa. So the sort of account they give may suddenly come out in a big poem like Dante's, or it may come out in a Newtonian concept. In other words, the palm isn't equally given in each generation. But I feel that they're linked hand in hand in this attack on what the meaning of it all is.

The meaning of it all: the meaning of the pattern of nature, and of man's place in nature. Durrell's quest is also Salam's quest, and Saarinen's, and Paolozzi's. It is the quest of every man, whether scientist or artist or man in the street.

The driving force in man is the search for freedom from the limitations which nature has imposed. Man, unlike the animals, is able to free himself. The first crude attempts were already made by Stone Age man with his tools and paintings. Now, twenty thousand years later, we are still struggling for freedom. We try to reach it by understanding the meaning of things. Our age tries to see things from the inside, and to find the structure, the architecture which underlies the surface appearance of things. We command nature by understanding her logic.

Our age has found some unexpected turns in the logic of nature. How atoms evolve, much like living species. How living things code and pass on their pattern of life, much like a machine. How the rigorous laws of nature are averaged from the million uncertainties of atoms and individuals. How time itself is an averaging and a disordering, a steady loss of the exceptional.

How life opposes time by constantly re-creating the exceptional. And how profoundly our ideas of so safe and absolute a concept as time once seemed to be can be changed by the vision of one man, who saw and proved that time is relative.

Above all, our age has shown how these ideas, and all human ideas, are created by one human gift: imagination. We leave the animals behind because they have no language of images. Imagination is the gift by which man creates a vision of the world.

We in the twentieth century have a vision which unifies not only the physical world but the world of living things and the world of the mind. We have a much greater sense of person than any other age. We are more free than our ancestors from the limitations both of our physical and of our psychological environments.

We are persons in our own right as no-one was before us. It is not only that we can travel into space and under the oceans. Nor is it only that psychology has made us more at home with ourselves. It is a real sense of unity with nature. We see nature not as a thing but as a process, profound and beautiful; and we see it from the inside. We belong to it. This above all is what science has given us: the vision of our age.

ACKNOWLEDGEMENTS

I owe a debt first to the British Broadcasting Corporation, which presented these programmes beautifully: that is, with exact attention to their scientific meaning and yet with a rich sense of their visual content. In particular, I am indebted to the Executive Producer, Humphrey Fisher, and the Producer, Bill Wright; to my scientific consultants, Dr. Michael Fisher and Lewis Walpert; and to those who helped me to put my ideas into images and words, Gerald Leach and Bryan Silcock.

Next, I owe a debt to the scientific and other colleagues who joined me in these programmes,

Mrs. A. R. Jonckheere
Prof. Barbel Inhelder
Prof. H. Bondi, F.R.S.
Dr. H. Friedman
Prof. L. S. Penrose, F.R.S.
Dr. D. J. Pierse
Dr. Paul Wood, O.B.E.
Prof. D. R. Newth
Dr. R. A. Hinde
Dr. H. J. Hay
Eduardo Paolozzi
Prof. Abdus Salam, F.R.S.
Lawrence Durrell
Eero Saarinen

And finally, I am indebted to many other colleagues who discussed the themes of the programmes with me, and who helped me with advice and with material. Among these were particularly,

Dr. D. K. Butt
Prof. H. G. Callan
Dr. O. G. Fahmy
Dr. C. E. Ford
Dr. H. B. D. Kettlewell
Dr. Antoinette Pirie
Dr. J. Maynard Smith
Dr. H. K. Weinbren
Barbara Hepworth, C.B.E.
Henry Moore, O.M., C.H.
Reg Butler
John Skeaping, R.A.

This book is a record of their work as well as mine, and I am glad that it gives me the occasion to set down my thanks to them all.